Permanent Wood Foundations

Canadian
Wood
Council

Conseil
canadien
du bois

ISBN 0-921628-19-6

5M92-12

Photograph credits:
Roy Grogan Photography, and
Council of Forest Industries
of British Columbia

Printed in Canada on recycled paper.

Preface

This publication comments and expands on the requirements for permanent wood foundations (PWF) found in Canadian Standards Association (CSA) standards CAN/CSA-O86.1, *Engineering Design in Wood,* and CAN/CSA-S406, *Construction of Preserved Wood Foundations.**

CAN/CSA-S406 is the construction standard for PWFs which is referenced in Part 9 of the *National Building Code of Canada* and in provincial building codes. CAN/CSA-S406 applies to buildings up to two storeys above the foundation and having a building area not exceeding 600 square metres. This does not exclude PWFs in larger buildings, using the same principles of design, provided building code requirements are met.

For conditions that go beyond the scope of CAN/CSA-S406 and this publication (see Design Assumptions, Appendix), similar details may be used provided they are based on accepted engineering principles that ensure a level of performance equivalent to that set forth in CAN/CSA-S406 and this publication. CAN/CSA-O86.1 and *The Wood Design Manual* published by the Canadian Wood Council contain information on the engineering design of PWFs.

* The “P” in PWF has been used to represent both “preserved” and “permanent”. In this publication, the term “permanent” is used.

Table of Contents

Table of Contents

Introduction

PWFs offer warm, dry and economical living space in homes from Halifax (above) to Vancouver (below)

1.0 Introduction

History

The permanent wood foundation (PWF) is a complete wood frame foundation or crawlspace for low-rise, residential, industrial, commercial and other types of buildings. PWFs are built using lumber and plywood, pressure-treated with approved wood preservatives.

Experience with the use of treated wood in ground contact dates back to 1938 when the U.S. Forest Products Laboratory installed treated wood stakes in areas prone to fungal and termite attack. Regular inspections of the stakes since that time have shown that wood treated to required retentions gives excellent service.

The first homes built on PWFs treated with water-borne preservatives were constructed in Alberta in 1967 and are still performing well. In the early 1970s material and certification standards for preservative treatment of wood were prepared, and a CWC Construction Guide was published in 1974. In addition, a plant certification system was set up to ensure that treating plants were operating correctly.

Canada Mortgage and Housing Corporation accepted the PWF for use under the National Housing Act in the early 1970s. In 1975 the Ontario Building Code permitted the use of PWFs. In 1983 the PWF construction standard, CAN/CSA-S406 was published and referenced in the national and provincial building codes. CWC replaced its Construction Guide with text files, such as this one, to provide a commentary on CAN/CSA-S406.

Advantages

PWFs have significant advantages over other types of foundations:

- In-place framing for easy and economical insulating and finishing.
- Energy savings because of high insulation levels of PWFs (about 20% of heat loss can go through the foundation).
- Dry, comfortable living space provided by a superior drainage system (which does not require weeping tile).
- Increased living space since drywall can be attached directly to foundation wall studs.
- Good performance under severe conditions such as earthquake loading.
- Resistance to damage, such as cracks, from cold weather.
- Adaptable to most building designs, including crawl spaces, additions and walk-out basements.
- Cost savings in construction, particularly when comparing costs of fully insulated and finished basements.
- One trade required for more efficient construction scheduling.
- Buildable during winter using minimal measures around the footings to protect them from freezing.
- Rapid construction, whether framed on site or pre-fabricated off-site.
- Long life, based on field and engineering experience.

The Ontario Ministry of Energy estimated that full-height insulation of a conventional basement in southern Ontario would result in about 700 kg less CO_2 emissions for a typical gas-heated house. Code requirements for full-height insulation are coming, and they will result in lower monthly heating bills. With a PWF, the initial construction cost is less and the savings can be increased by using more insulation.

Glossary of Terms Used in This Book

Backfill height:
: the height of soil backfill measured from the top of the footing to the exterior grade level at any particular point. For a crawl space with a trenched footing, backfill height is the difference between exterior and interior backfill heights at any particular point

End wall:
: the exterior wall parallel to the floor joists – the wall not supporting the floor joists

Framing strap:
: a strip of 0.9mm (20 gauge) galvanized metal, at least 38 x 400mm (1-1/2 x 16 in.) in size, fastened to wood with 76mm (3 in.) nails

Granular drainage layer:
: the continuous layer of crushed stone or gravel used to drain the bottom of the foundation and to distribute the load from the footing to the soil

Jack stud:
: a less than full height stud that is nailed to a full height stud to support the end of a lintel or beam and to transfer vertical loads to the footing

Knee wall:
: a less than full height wall used outside the main foundation wall to support brick or stone siding or other loads

Side wall:
: the exterior wall perpendicular to the floor joists – the wall supporting the floor joists

Sill:
: the horizontal member forming the bottom of the rough frame openings of windows and doors

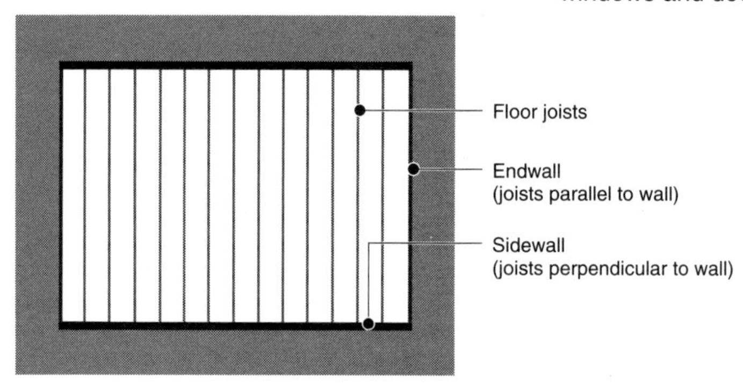

The PWF System

2

2.0 The PWF System

System Description

The PWF is a loadbearing wood-frame system designed as a foundation for light-frame construction. It is well suited for single family homes, room additions, multi-level residential buildings, industrial, agricultural and commercial buildings. Although similar to regular wood-frame construction, there are some differences.

All lumber and plywood in the PWF is pressure treated with water-borne preservatives. Nails and straps must be corrosion resistant.

The walls are designed to resist soil pressure loads in addition to the normal vertical loads of snow, floor and dead loads. The soil loads are transferred from the PWF walls into the main floor and basement floor. Vertical loads are distributed to the supporting soil through a wood or concrete footing resting on a granular drainage layer of crushed stone or gravel (Figure 2.1).

Improved moisture control methods around and beneath the foundation result in comfortable, dry living space below grade. The foundation is placed on a granular drainage layer which extends 300mm beyond the footings. Porous backfill, either the native soil if well draining or new material, is brought up to within 300mm (12 in.) of finished grade and the remaining space filled with less permeable or native soil sloped away from the house.

The porous drainage material directs ground water to below the basement, thus preventing hydrostatic pressure and leaks in the basement walls or floor. A sump is provided, in accordance with the building code, and is drained by mechanical or gravity means.

No drainage tile is needed around the footings as this may impede the flow of water (Figure 2.2 and 2.3). The granular drainage layer can accommodate a large influx of water during peak storm conditions. It also provides a large surface area for water to percolate into the subsoil.

Caulking between all wall panels, and between the walls and footings, and a moisture barrier applied to the outside of the walls provide additional protection against moisture. The result is a dry basement that can be easily insulated and finished for maximum comfort and energy conservation.

Figure 2.1
Loads and reactions in foundations

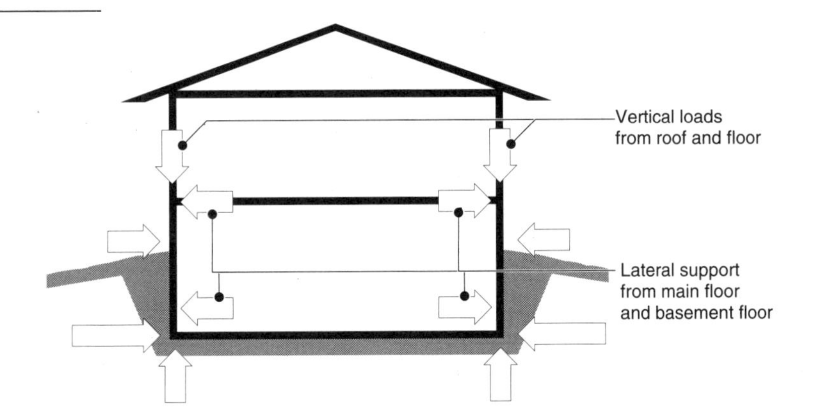

Figure 2.2
Types of permanent wood foundations

Note:
Throughout this publication, shaded wood denotes treated wood. Unshaded wood denotes wood that has not been treated.

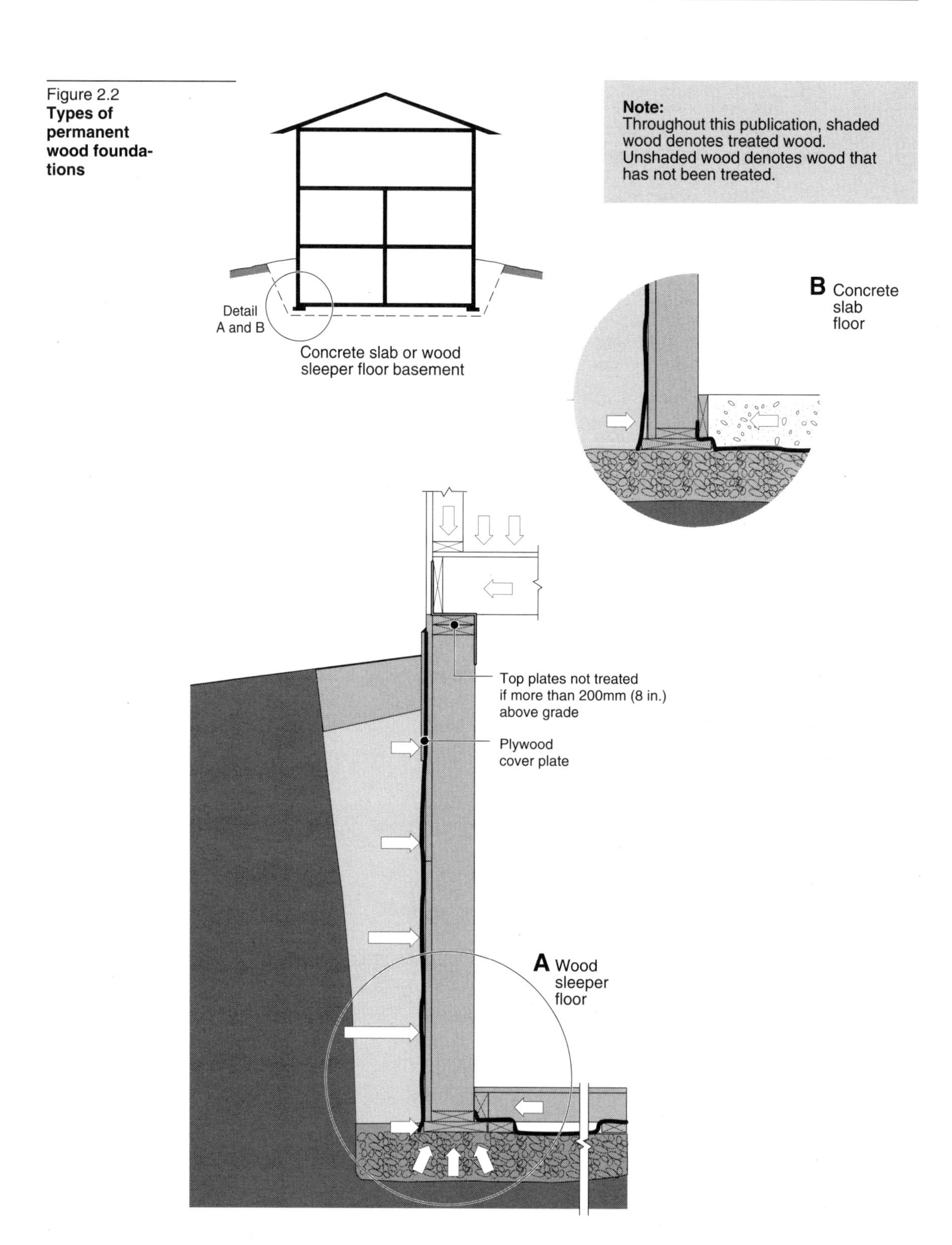

Figure 2.3
Types of permanent wood foundations

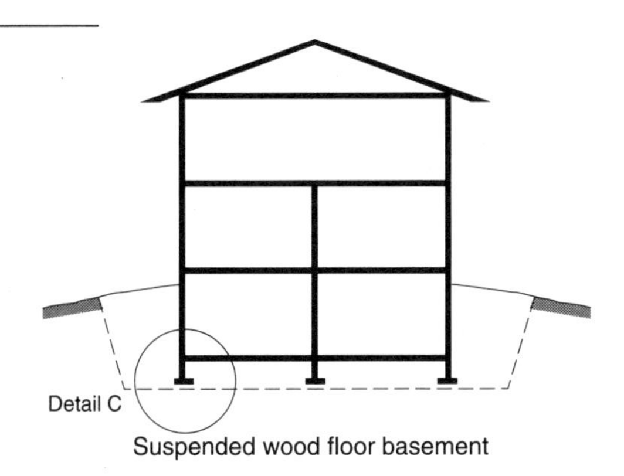

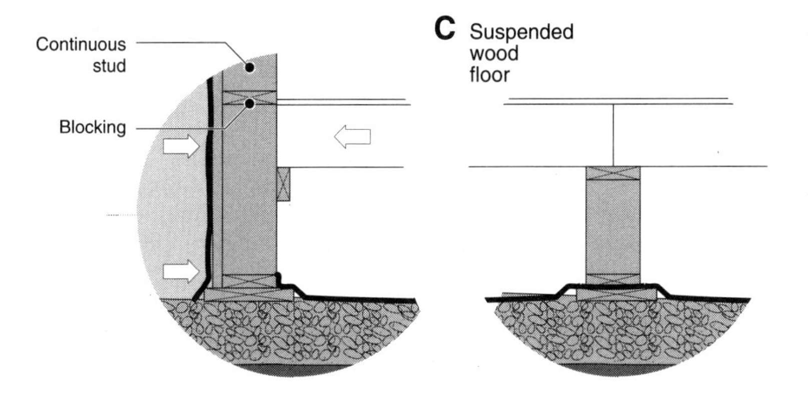

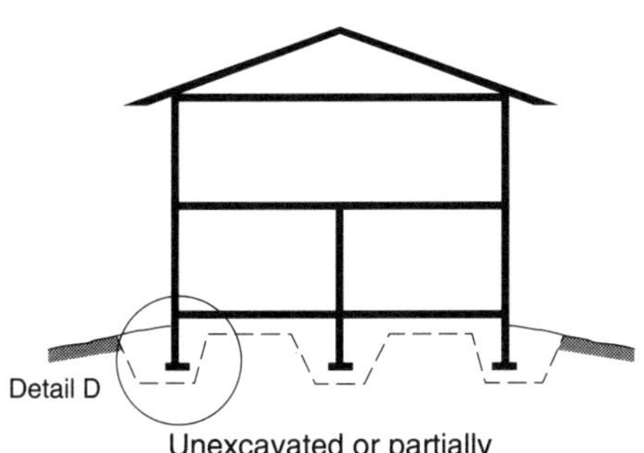

Note: In a partially excavated crawl space, the interior grade is only slightly lower than the exterior grade.

In a fully excavated crawl space, a floor system or other form of support should be installed at or near the base of the crawl space wall.

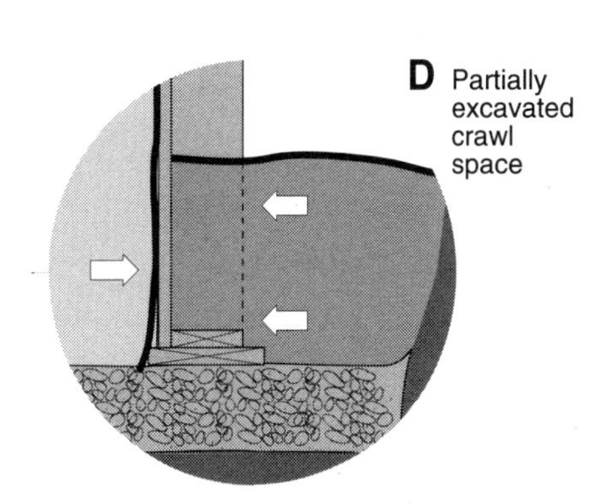

Design Requirements

Design information in this publication is based on CSA standards S406 and O86.1. CAN/CSA-S406, *Construction of Preserved Wood Foundations,* describes the required materials and methods of construction of permanent wood foundations.

CAN/CSA-S406 is referenced in Part 9 (Section 9.15) of the *National Building Code of Canada (NBCC)* and applies to buildings not exceeding 600m^2 (about 6000 sq. ft.) in building area and not more than two storeys high.

Buildings that exceed these limits must be designed according to standard CAN/CSA-O86.1, *Engineering Design in Wood,* which is referenced in Part 4 of the NBCC. The standard includes some specific information relating to PWFs.

The stud wall selection tables in this publication take into account the influence of floor loads, roof snow loads, dead loads and lateral backfill loads, which generally govern the design. (See Appendix for a complete list of design assumptions.)

Tables are also provided for increased perimeter nail spacing requirements in PWF plywood wall sheathing in cases where backfill heights are uneven around the perimeter of the building, that is, more than about 600mm (24 in.) difference front-to-back.

Buildings that exceed these limits or vary from the design assumptions listed in the Appendix may be built provided building code requirements are met. This usually requires the assistance of an engineer.

PWFs, as with all foundations, should bear on soils capable of carrying the weight of the building so that excessive settlement does not occur. The soil should be free draining and not have swelling characteristics that could cause significant damage to the building.

A qualified engineer should be consulted to design the footings and the foundation in the presence of soils with low bearing capacity such as soft clays, soft sands, peat or fill, excessively swelling clays, or on permafrost.

Types of PWFs

PWF with Wood Sleeper Floor or Concrete Slab

The most common type of PWF floor system consists of a pressure-treated wood floor resting on pressure-treated wood sleepers, or a concrete slab floor. The foundation walls are roughly 2.4 to 3m (8 to 10 ft.) high (Figure 2.2).

PWF with Suspended Floor

The suspended floor PWF uses wood frame walls 3 to 3.6m (10 to 12 ft.) high with a wood joist floor attached inside the foundation walls about 600mm (24 in.) above the gravel bed. The suspended floor is suited to split-entry homes and where deep footings are required to reach stable bearing soil.

PWF Crawl Space

An unexcavated, partially excavated or fully excavated crawl space is used where a full basement can not be built or is not wanted, such as on a site with a high water table or on solid rock.

Materials

All treated lumber and plywood in PWFs must bear a "PWF" stamp to indicate that they have been specially treated for in-ground use.

End-cut treated lumber must be brushed or soaked with field preservative.

3.0 Materials

Treated Materials

With some exceptions, all lumber and plywood used in permanent wood foundations must be pressure treated with preservatives in accordance with Canadian Standards Association (CSA) standard CAN/CSA-O80.15, *Preservative Treatment of Wood for Building Foundation Systems, Basements and Crawl Spaces by Pressure Process.*

Untreated wood may be used for:

- exterior wall top plates more than 200mm (8 in.) above the adjacent exterior grade,
- floor structures more than 300mm (12 in.) above the granular drainage layer or interior ground level of a ventilated crawl space,
- interior columns and partitions above a suspended wood floor, wood sleeper floor or concrete slab floor where, in the case of the latter, the column is separated from the concrete by a dampproofing material such as polyethylene.

CAN/CSA O80.15 requires a higher level of preservative treatment for PWF material than is provided for regular treated wood in ground contact such as in fences and decks.

Treating plants are qualified by recognized inspection agencies to stamp PWF wood. To indicate its higher level of treatment, all PWF lumber and plywood is marked with a special stamp or qualification mark (Figure 3.1) that confirms that the treating facility is qualified and inspected under CAN/CSA-O322, *Procedure for Certification of Pressure-Treated Wood Materials for Use in Preserved Wood Foundations,* to treat wood for PWFs.

Once qualified under CAN/CSA-O322, the treating plants are subject to periodic inspection. Regular treated wood used for fences and decks looks similar to that used for PWFs, therefore only treated lumber and plywood bearing the qualification stamp should be used in PWFs.

Not all species are treatable. Lumber used in PWFs must conform to the list of treatable species given in Table 3.1.

3 Materials

Figure 3.1
Facsimile of qualification mark

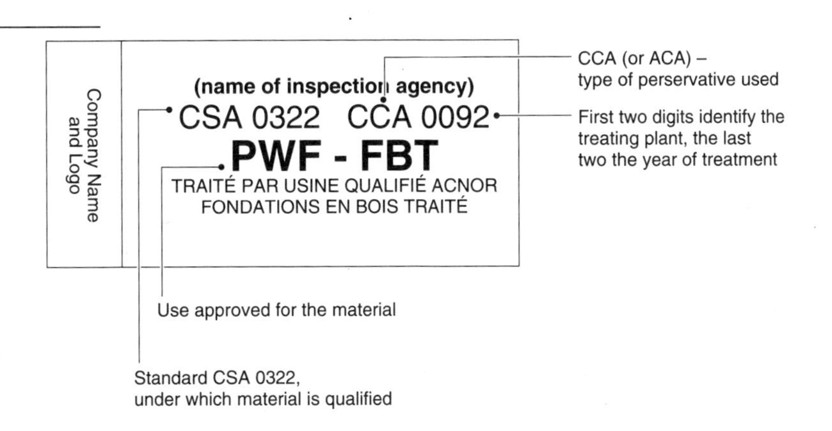

Types of Preservative and Disposal

The most common preservative used to treat wood for PWFs, decks, fences and other outdoor uses is chromated copper arsenate or CCA which gives wood the common green colour. It is very different from the older creosote and pentachlorophenol preservatives.

The latter two are carried in petroleum-based solvents and are used for applications such as poles, piles or railroad ties. Both are held within the cell cavities of the wood but are not chemically bonded to the wood. This leaves an oily surface which is not well suited to PWFs.

CCA is a water-based preservative that is forced into the wood under pressure. The preservative bonds chemically with the wood so that after a brief curing period it will not leach or off-gas to any significant degree. PWF-treated lumber and plywood is dried after treatment to facilitate this curing and give a clean surface to the wood.

There are some common safety rules for working with treated wood. Gloves should be worn to protect against splinters during construction. Other precautions include wearing a dust mask when cutting the wood and washing hands after handling it. Waste treated wood should be buried, not burned, since burning the wood concentrates the preservative in the ash. Short, cut-off pieces can be used as blocking in floor and wall construction.

Cutting and Field Treating

Treated lumber should not be cut lengthwise or notched since this will expose untreated material and change the grade of the lumber. Cross cutting of treated lumber is permitted as is cutting of plywood since these surfaces will readily absorb brushed-on field preservative.

The cut surfaces must be treated with a copper naphthenate preservative prepared with a solvent conforming to CAN/CSA-O80.201, *Standard for Hydrocarbon Solvents for Preservatives.* Proper field preservative is usually available from building supply retailers. The cut surface is brushed, dipped or soaked until the wood absorbs no more preservative.

Cross-cutting may not always be necessary, for example, a wood footing plate that extends beyond a corner need not be cut. Studs cut to length should be installed with their cut ends up.

Lumber

Lumber used in PWFs conforms to CAN/CSA-O141, *Softwood Lumber,* and bears a grade stamp from a recognized grading agency indicating the species, grade and mill number.

Studs used in the foundation walls are required to be No. 2 grade or better. Grades for floor joists in sleeper floors can be found in regular span tables published in the national or provincial building codes.

Table 3.1 **Treatable lumber species**

	Treatable species	Grade stamp identification
Species Group 1	Coast Douglas fir	D Fir (N)
	Western hemlock	W Hem(N) or Hem-Fir(N)
	Amabilis fir	Am Fir(N) or Hem-Fir(N)
	Lodgepole pine	L Pine(N)
	Jack Pine	J Pine(N)
	Alpine Fir	Alpine Fir(N)
	Balsam Fir	B Fir(N)
	Ponderosa Pine	P Pine
Species Group 2	Red pine	R Pine(N)
	Western white pine	W.W.Pine
	Eastern white pine	East White Pine or (EW Pine) (N)
	Eastern hemlock	Hem-Tam (N)

Plywood

Treated plywood for exterior wall sheathing and subflooring in wood sleeper floors is unsanded, exterior type with at least four plies and limited to the following species: western hemlock, amabilis fir, grand fir and coast Douglas fir. All plywood should bear markings identifying it as "Hem-Fir" plywood and conform to: CAN/CSA-O121-M, *Douglas Fir Plywood* or CAN/CSA-O151-M, *Canadian Softwood Plywood.*

Plywood panels marked "COFI Exterior DFP-Hem Fir" or "COFI Exterior CSP-Hem Fir" meet both the strength and treatability requirements for PWFs. Plywood conforming to CAN/CSA-O121-M or CAN/CSA-O151-M but not identified as "Hem-Fir" may contain other species that do not readily accept preservative treatment and should not be used.

Nails and Staples

All metal connectors used in the construction of PWFs must be corrosion resistant. Nails can be either hot-dipped galvanized or stainless steel conforming to CAN/CSA-B111, *Wire Nails, Spikes and Staples.* Staples must be stainless steel and have a minimum diameter or thickness of 1.6 mm with a 9.5mm crown, conforming to American Iron and Steel Institute Type 304 or 316.

Attaching plywood sheathing to studs using staples is not permitted when backfill heights are uneven since, in these cases, there will be greater stress on the fasteners.

Framing Anchors and Straps

Framing anchors and straps in contact with treated materials must be hot-dipped galvanized in accordance with ASTM Standard A446, Steel Sheet, Zinc-Coated (Galvanized by the Hot-Dip Process), Structural (Physical) Quality. They must be used at the top of every stud where nailing alone will not transfer the loads, usually where backfill heights exceed 1.5m (5 ft.).

A framing strap is made of 20-gauge galvanized metal, at least 38 x 400mm (1-1/2 x 16 in.) fastened to the wood with 76mm (3 in.) nails of the type described above. Framing anchors should be fastened in accordance with the specifications of the manufacturer.

Caulking

Caulking applied between plywood panel joints, between wall and footings, and elsewhere should be capable of providing a watertight seal, have a long expected service life without drying or hardening and be workable at low temperatures. The caulking should also be compatible with the exterior moisture barrier.

The caulking fills tiny gaps between plywood and wall studs. The caulking is backed on three sides by the stud and panel edges, and so is not normally subjected to significant stresses and strains.

CAN/CSA-S406 recommends two types of caulkings:

- CAN/CGSB-19.13-M, *Sealing Compound, One Component, Elastomeric, Chemical Curing*
- CGSB-19-GP-14M, *Sealing Compound, One Component, Butyl-Polyisobutylene Polymer Base, Solvent Curing*

The butyl caulkings (CGSB-19-GP-14M) are minimum requirements and have performed well in PWFs. They are relatively inexpensive, stable, slow-curing, moisture-resistant and have a maximum movement (expansion) capability of up to 7.5%.

Building supply retailers usually sell caulkings appropriate for PWF use. A Qualified Products List of brand name caulkings that conform to CAN/CGSB-19.13-M and CGSB-19-GP-14M may be obtained for a nominal cost from:

Canadian General Standards Board (CGSB)
Department of Supply and Services
222 Queen Street
14th Floor
Ottawa, ON
K1A 1G6

Moisture Barriers

A moisture barrier is applied to the below-ground portion of the PWF walls to deflect ground moisture down to the gravel bed during peak storm and run-off periods. CAN/CSA-S406 requires the use of a minimum 0.15mm (6 mil) polyethylene moisture barrier conforming to standard CAN2-51.34-M, *Vapour Barrier, Polyethylene Sheet, for Use in Building Construction.* A moisture barrier is not required for garage frost walls, knee walls and crawl spaces with trenched footings.

Other barriers, combinations of films and coatings can be used subject to the approval of the building authority having jurisdiction. These barriers must also be compatible with the treated wood and the caulking and have good adhesion to the PWF sheathing.

The *Alberta Building Code,* for example, permits the use of two coats of bituminous dampproofing coatings as the moisture barrier in place of polyethylene. The PWF construction standard S406 references three types:

- CAN/CGSB-37.2, *Emulsified Asphalt, Mineral Colloid Type, Unfilled, for Dampproofing and Waterproofing and for Roof Coatings*
- 37-GP-6Ma, *Asphalt, Cutback, Unfilled for Dampproofing*
- CAN/CGSB-37.16, *Filled Cutback Asphalt for Dampproofing and Waterproofing*

Where they are permitted, these coatings must also comply with the requirements of the authority having jurisdiction.

Bituminous dampproofing coatings are sometimes used with other films, such as polyethylene, which are pressed into the dampproofing. Materials used in combination must be compatible. For example, some types of caulking should not be used in combination with dampproofing containing petroleum-based solvents. Bituminous cements are recommended for use as caulking with bituminous coatings.

Manufactured drainage mats and membranes or appropriate forms of insulation may be applied over the moisture barrier to enhance drainage and insulation value and to protect the polyethylene during backfill. Drainage mats must have a vertical water permeability at least equal to that of coarse clean sand. These materials are optional in most cases, but may be required by local conditions.

Backfill

Soil from the foundation excavation may be used for backfill if it has medium or better drainage characteristics. These include sands, gravels, and some mixtures of sand/gravel/clay. Backfill delivered to the site must also be free draining material. Backfill should be free of debris, frozen clumps and rocks larger than 150mm (6 in.).

Granular Drainage Layer

The granular drainage layer beneath the foundation floor and footings must be clean crushed stone or gravel containing not more than 10% of fine material that will pass through a 4mm (1/8 in.) sieve, and no material larger than 40mm (1-1/2 in.). The drainage layer also acts as a continuous footing to distribute vertical loads to the subsoil.

Table 3.2
Metric and Imperial sizes

	Metric, mm	Imperial, in.
Lumber	38 x 38	2 x 2
	38 x 89	2 x 4
	38 x 140	2 x 6
	38 x 184	2 x 8
	38 x 235	2 x 10
	38 x 286	2 x 12
Screed board	19 x 64	1 x 3
Joist/stud spacing	300	12
	400	16
	600	24
Nail lengths	51	2
	76	3
	89	3-1/2
Staple sizes	1.6 diameter or thickness	1/16
	9.5	3/8
Polyethylene thickness	0.15	6 mil (0.006)
Plywood	1220 x 2440	4 x 8 ft.

Selecting and Preparing the Site

The granular drainage layer of a PWF provides good drainage and dry living space.

4.0 Selecting and Preparing the Site

Selecting the Site

The choice of building site has great effect on the performance of any foundation. Building in low-lying areas or on flood plains may present problems during the wet seasons. Figure 4.1 provides some guidance on building location.

Figure 4.1
Choosing a building site

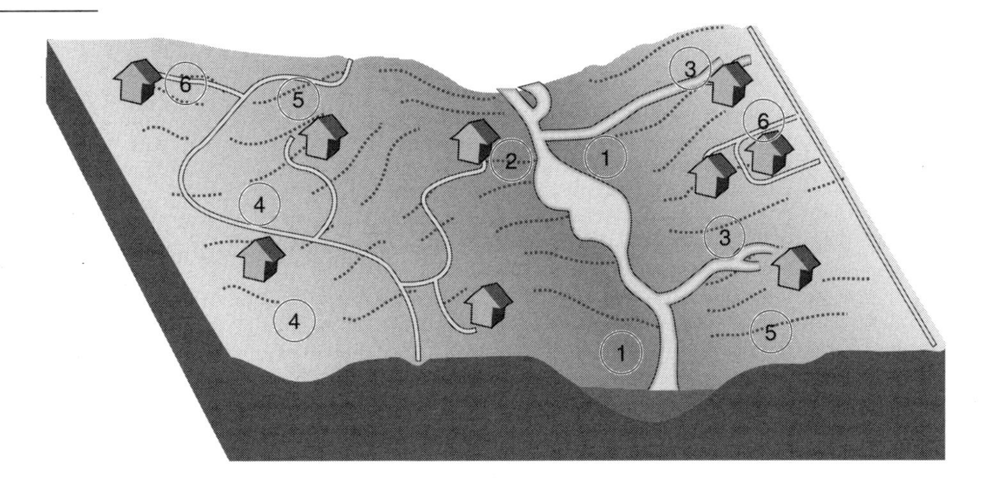

Area 1	Flood plain, subject to flooding during heavy storms
Area 2	Alluvial fan where soil has been formed by water eroding material from the watershed above and depositing it near the mouth of the waterway
Area 3	Upland waterway where water flowing from higher surrounding land will concentrate. Should not be used unless an adequate ditch or diversion terrace has been constructed to divert water.
Area 4	Low area where water accumulates from higher surrounding areas. These soils remain wet and spongy for long periods.
Area 5	Steep hillside where soil may be shallow. Some areas are subject to severe slippage. Soils could be stable, or in some cases could move through gravity or by water erosion. The problem can be solved by studying the soils and avoiding the bad ones.
Area 6	Deep, well-drained soil found on ridgetops and gently sloping hillsides. Generally these areas have the smallest water management problems and are usually the best building sites.

Excavation

Excavation methods should conform to those described in the appropriate building code. Before placing the gravel bed and footings, dig a trench for service and sump drain lines.

Backfill the trenches and compact once the lines are installed (Figure 4.2). Service lines may be run through the wall above the footing, but it is better practice to install service lines below the footings where possible.

Figure 4.2
Installation of footings and service lines

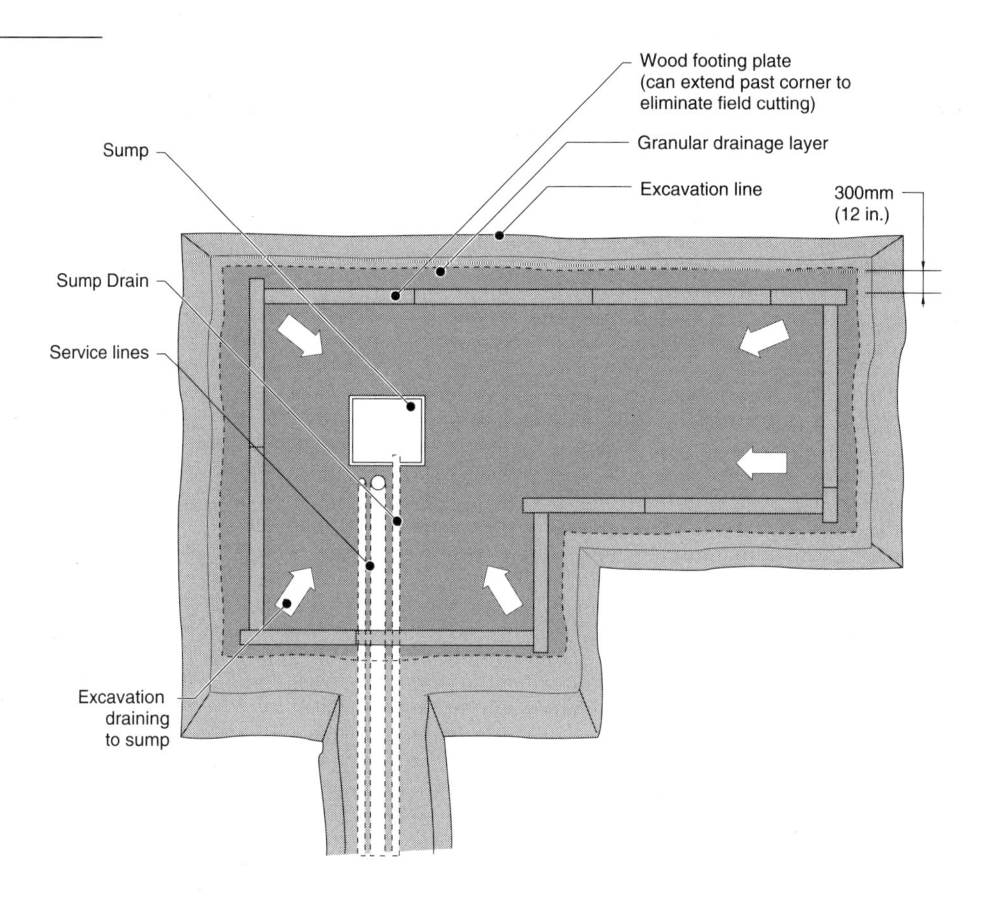

Sump

The PWF construction standard, CAN/CSA-S406, requires a sump pit to a depth of at least 750mm (2.5 ft.) below the top of the granular drainage layer constructed of poured concrete, concrete pipe, tile or pressure-treated wood.

The sump rests on and is surrounded by a 150mm (6 in.) layer of clean granular material (Figure 4.3).

Ground water flows by gravity into the sump from the bottom or through holes in the liner. The sump is drained by gravity or by sump pump through a 100mm (4 in.) line.

Figure 4.3
Granular drainage to sump

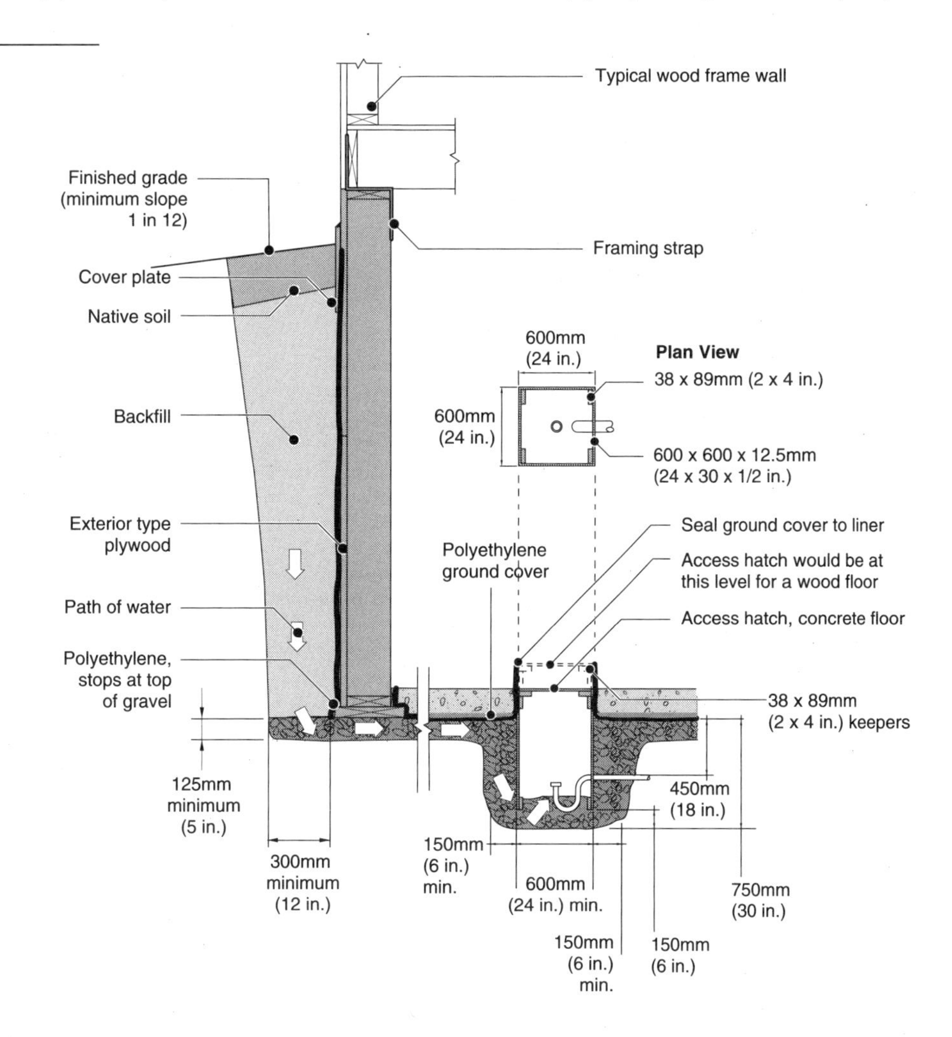

Granular Drainage Layer

The granular drainage layer serves three functions:

- surge storage basin to accommodate peak storage conditions,
- seepage pit to allow water to disperse into the soil below, and
- full area drainage of water from any point, especially from the footings.

After installing the service lines and sump, place a 125mm (5 in.) granular drainage layer over the undisturbed soil and extend it 300mm (12 in.) beyond the footing. It is good practice to compact the drainage layer in the locations of the footings, particularly where the depth of the layer exceeds 200mm (8 in.).

If soil becomes mixed with the drainage layer because of wet site conditions, deposit more granular material so that the top 125mm (5 in.) is free of soil.

Trenched footings, as used for garages and in unexcavated crawl spaces, must be drained to a sump pit or to the outside, such as a dry ditch, where the accumulation of water in the trench may result in frost heaving of the supported structure (see Chapter 10). This is particularly important on sites having certain types of clay soils that expand when wet, or in conditions of excessive humidity in enclosed crawl spaces and below floors.

Soils

All foundations, regardless of their type or size, are supported by the undisturbed soil below the footings. The bearing capacity of the soil (its ability to support the building), soil drainage characteristics, and height and seasonal changes in the water table affect the performance of foundations. The design assumptions listed in the Appendix provide minimum soil bearing capacity and maximum lateral soil loads for PWFs.

Soils with low bearing capacity, poor drainage characteristics, and high frost heave and swelling potential are not suitable for foundation construction. Soils that swell when wet can subject a foundation to higher than expected lateral loads.

Table 4.1 provides a general guideline of the suitability of soils in construction. An engineer experienced in soils analysis should be consulted if there is uncertainty about soil characteristics of a building site.

Table 4.1
Soil classification

Classification	Description
Fill	Soil that has been moved. Potential problems include lack of bearing support, possible contamination and unpredictable behaviour.
Organic soils	Soil containing topsoil, peat or alluvium. Potential problems include voids created by decay of organic material, lack of bearing support and presence of organic gases.
Clayey soils	Common soil type, identified by its cohesiveness. Forms clumps when squeezed in the hand. Bearing strength may be affected by excavation. Potential problems include soft clays leading to settlement or expansion, and the effects of water or frost after construction.
Granular soils	Sand or a mixture of sand and silt which usually show some cohesion when wet.Tend to be free-draining and stable, unless loose and/or poorly graded. Potential problem for loose sand is loss of support due to excavation and high water tables.
Glacial till	Tends to be free-draining and stable. Potential problems are large boulders and uneven size.
Rock	Very stable but may require blasting for removal.

Footings

Installing and levelling wood footings on the granular drainage layer.

5.0 Footings

Wood Footings

Continuous wood footings are usually more practical and economical than concrete footings for PWFs. Wood footings and the granular drainage layer act together to distribute loads from the structure to the undisturbed soil. Sizes of interior and exterior footings for different floor, siding and storey conditions are given in Table 5.1.

First, excavate to about 250mm (10 in.) below basement floor level and 300 to 450mm (12 to 18 in.) beyond the perimeter of the foundation. Set perimeter stringlines, then drive stakes every 1 to 2m (3 to 6 ft.) around the foundation, just inside the stringline. Use a transit to level the tops of the stakes and then deposit the gravel to the top of the stakes.

Table 5.1
Wood footing sizes (bearing on gravel bed)

Type of basement floor	Number of storeys	Type of exterior siding	Minimum sizes of wood footings, mm (in.) Supporting exterior walls	Supporting interior walls [1]
Wood sleeper or concrete slab	1	Conventional [2]	38 x 140 (2 x 6)	38 x 89 (2 x 4)
		Brick veneer	38 x 140 (2 x 6)	38 x 89 (2 x 4)
	2	Conventional	38 x 140 (2 x 6)	38 x 140 (2 x 6)
		Brick veneer (one storey)	38 x 184 (2 x 8)	38 x 140 (2 x 6)
		Brick veneer (two storeys)	38 x 235 (2 x 10) or Composite [3]	38 x 140 (2 x 6)
Suspended wood floor	1	Conventional	38 x 140 (2 x 6)	38 x 140 (2 x 6)
		Brick veneer	38 x 184 (2 x 8)	38 x 140 (2 x 6)
	2	Conventional	38 x 184 (2 x 8)	38 x 235 (2 x 10) or Composite [3]
		Brick veneer (one storey)	38 x 235 (2 x 10) or Composite [3]	38 x 235 (2 x 10) or Composite [3]
		Brick veneer (two storeys)	2 - 38 x 140 (2 x 6) [4]	38 x 235 (2 x 10) or Composite [3]

Notes:
1. Interior walls supported on the concrete slab do not require footings if concrete strength is adequate.
2. Conventional cladding includes wood, metal, plastic, stucco, and other non-masonry claddings.
3. Composite type footing consists of at least 38 x 140mm (2 x 6 in.) and 38 x 89mm (2 x 4 in.) lumber butted edge to edge and tied together with 12.5mm (1/2 in.) thick plywood and nails.
4. Two pieces of 38 x 140mm (2 x 6 in.) lumber butted edge to edge and tied together with 12.5mm (1/2 in.) thick plywood and nails.

Place wood footings directly on the levelled, compacted granular drainage layer and butt them together at end joints and wall intersections. Single member wood footings should be wide enough to support wall studs and sheathing, but should not extend more that 50mm (2 in.) on either side of the wall. A footing plate one size wider than the wall stud will usually suffice.

Where a knee wall is used to support brick veneer, the knee wall and main foundation wall can be supported on either separate footings or on a composite footing. Composite footings are made up of two individual footings placed side by side, and reinforced on the full width of the bottom face by pressure-treated plywood. The plywood must be at least 12.5mm thick (1/2 in.) and placed with the face grain perpendicular to the wall. The composite footing must be wide enough to provide a seat for the sheathing. (See Figure 6.8.)

Footing layouts should be planned to suit lumber lengths, or extend footings beyond corner intersections to avoid cutting. If the footings must be cut, saturate the cut ends with two coats of brush-on preservative.

Concrete Footings

Concrete footings supporting exterior and interior walls and columns should be sized and constructed according to the appropriate building code. Concrete footings can be placed on top of the gravel bed to allow drainage under the footing (Figure 5.1), or placed on the undisturbed soil with drainage paths provided through the footing to the granular drainage layer below the floor (Figure 5.2). These paths should have a minimal sectional area of 2500mm^2 (4 sq. in.). and a maximum spacing of 1200mm (4 ft.).

Figure 5.1
Concrete footing resting on a granular drainage layer

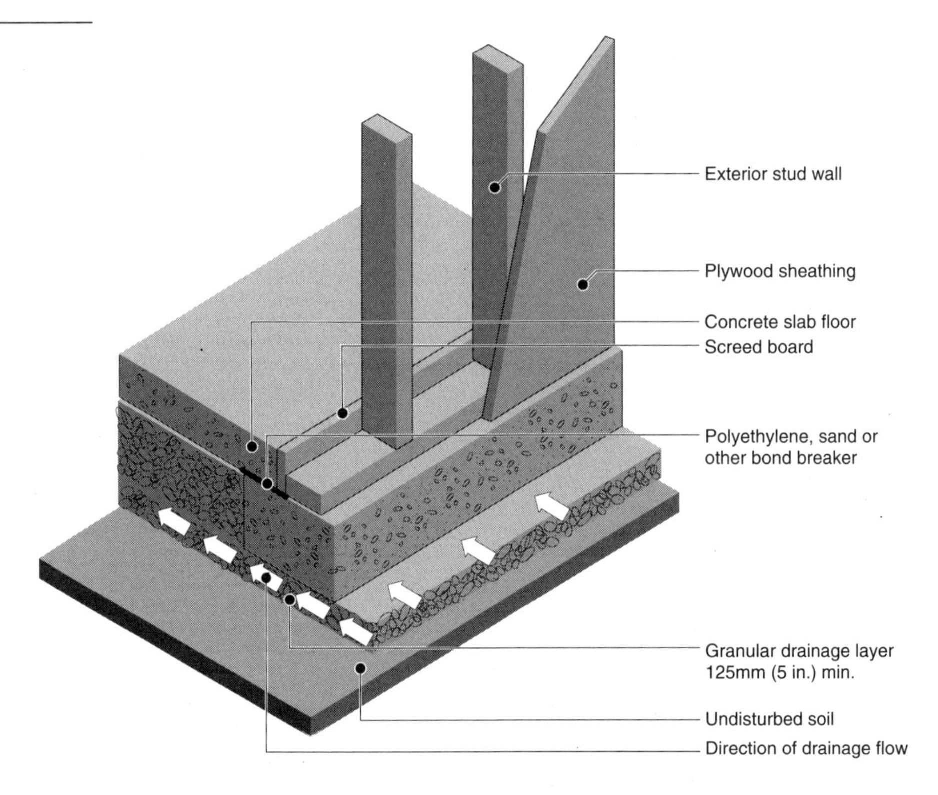

Figure 5.2
Concrete footing resting on undisturbed soil

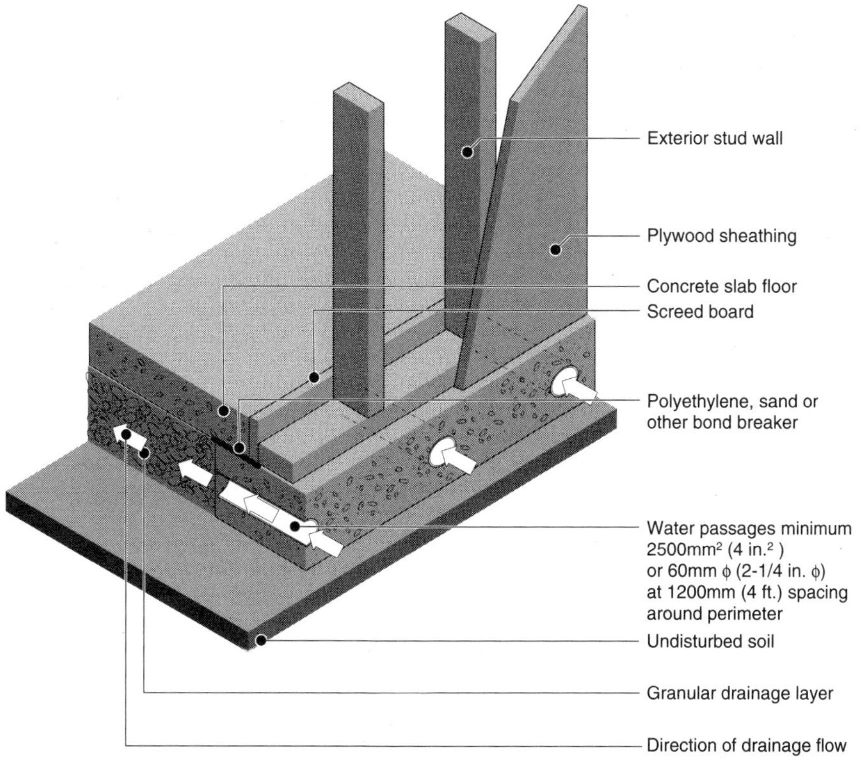

Exterior stud wall
Plywood sheathing
Concrete slab floor
Screed board
Polyethylene, sand or other bond breaker
Water passages minimum 2500mm^2 (4 in.^{2}) or 60mm ϕ (2-1/4 in. ϕ) at 1200mm (4 ft.) spacing around perimeter
Undisturbed soil
Granular drainage layer
Direction of drainage flow

Interior Footings

Interior footings are used to support interior load-bearing walls. Figures 5.3, 5.4, 5.5 and 5.6 show construction methods. Interior walls can either rest on a separate footing or on top of the basement floor. The latter method is more economical because the wall need not be treated.

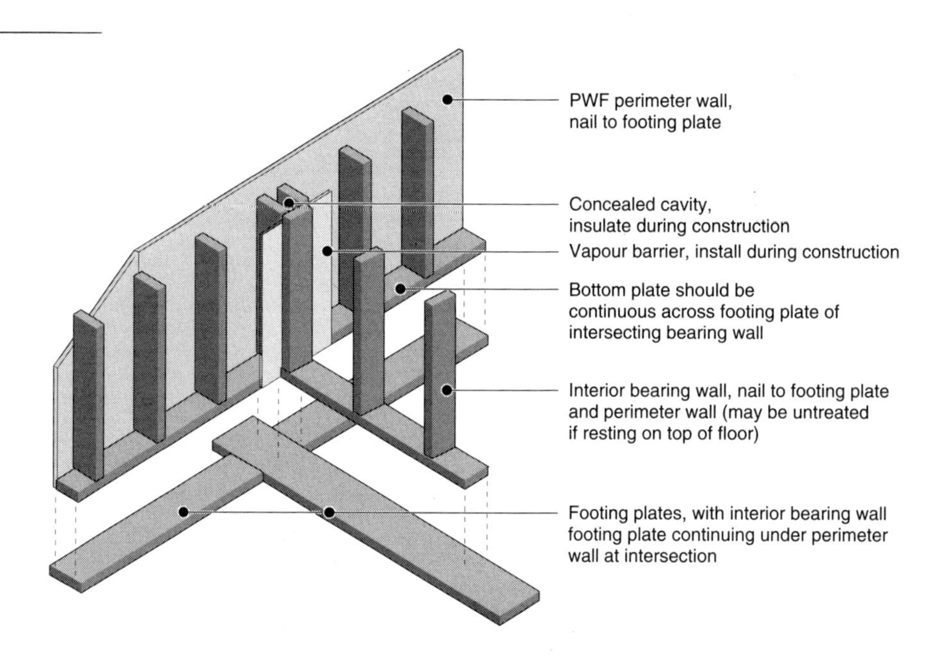

Figure 5.3
Interior bearing wall on a wood footing

Figure 5.4
Interior bearing wall resting on a floor

Joists perpendicular to bearing wall, wood sleeper floor

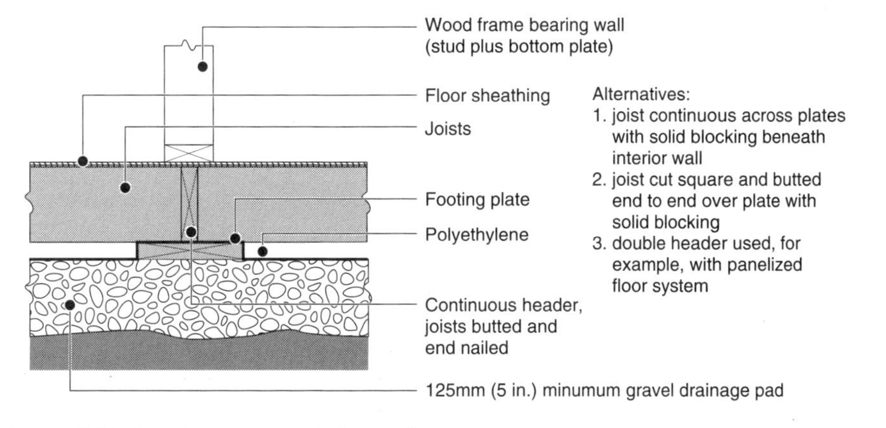

Joists parallel to bearing wall, wood sleeper floor

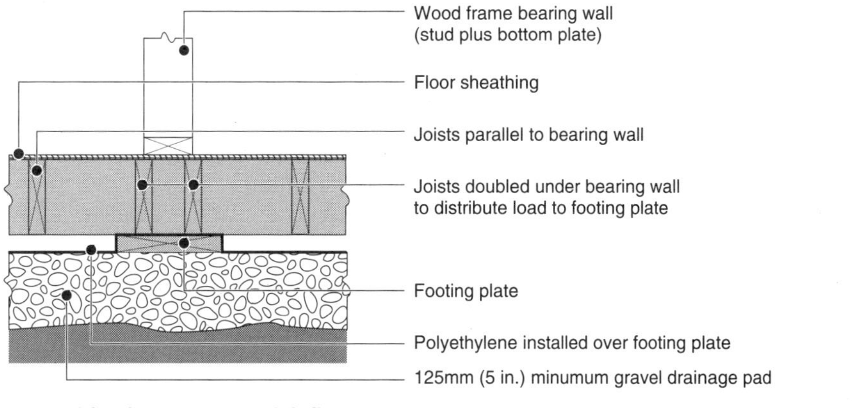

Built-up wood footing, concrete slab floor

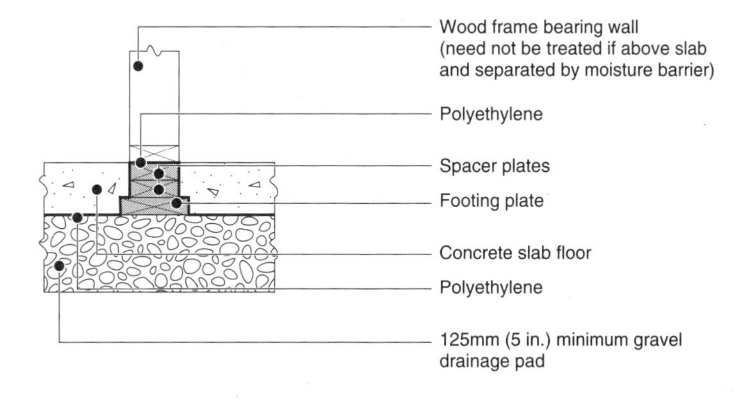

Figure 5.5
Interior bearing wall penetrating a wood sleeper floor

Sleeper floor: Footing / framing detail along wall

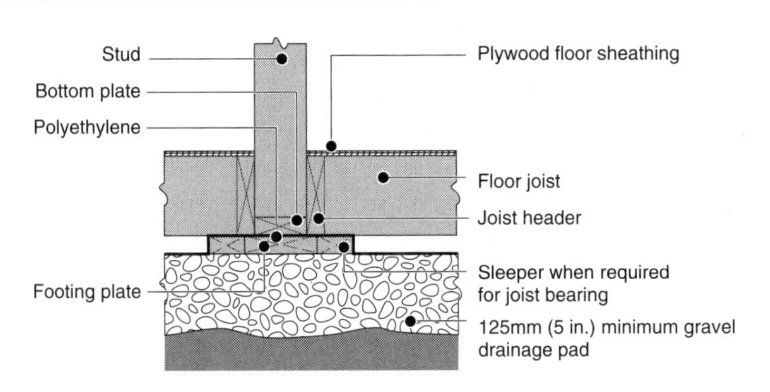

Sleeper floor: Footing / framing detail at wall opening

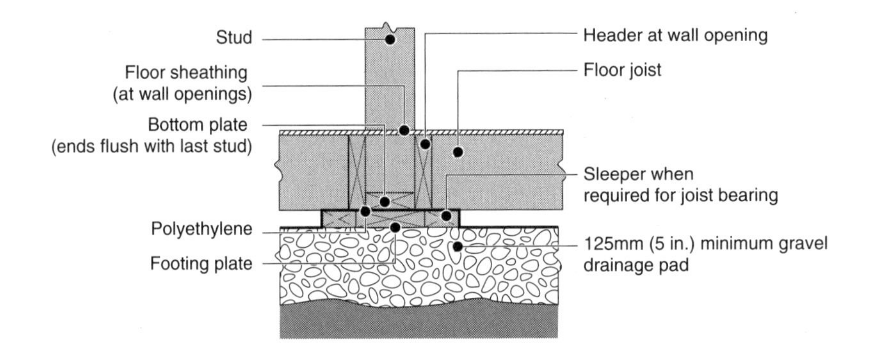

Figure 5.6
Interior bearing wall penetrating a concrete slab floor

Slab floor: Footing / framing detail along wall

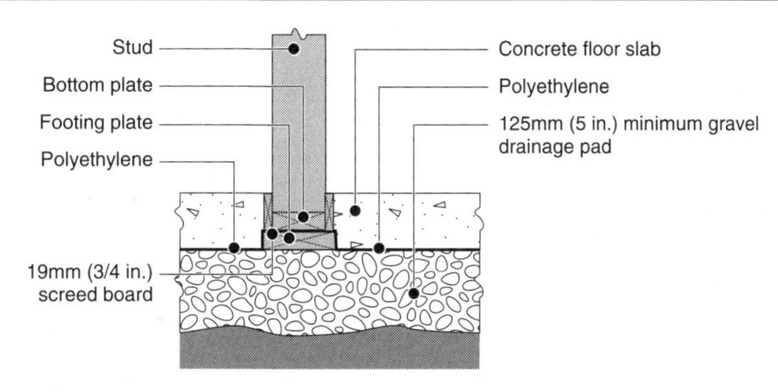

Slab floor: Footing / framing detail at wall opening

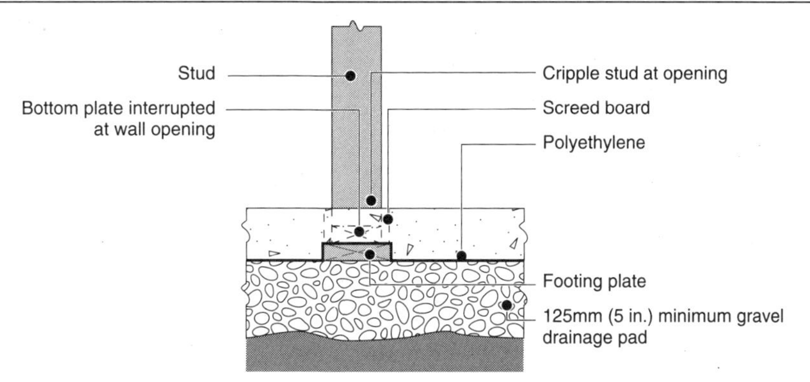

Column Footings

Columns used to support floor beams need special footings. Pressure-treated wood or concrete can be used for such footings. The size of wood column footings varies with building width and storey height (Table 5.2). The footings are constructed of two layers of treated lumber nailed together with the lumber pieces in each layer running perpendicular to the other.

A steel plate or column base is placed over the top layer to help transfer load from the column (Figures 5.7 and 5.8). Concrete column footings should be sized and constructed according to the building code.

Laying the footing on undisturbed soil is important to ensure full bearing. A thin layer of sand placed below the footing helps to provide uniform contact with the undisturbed soil.

Figure 5.7
Typical wood column footing

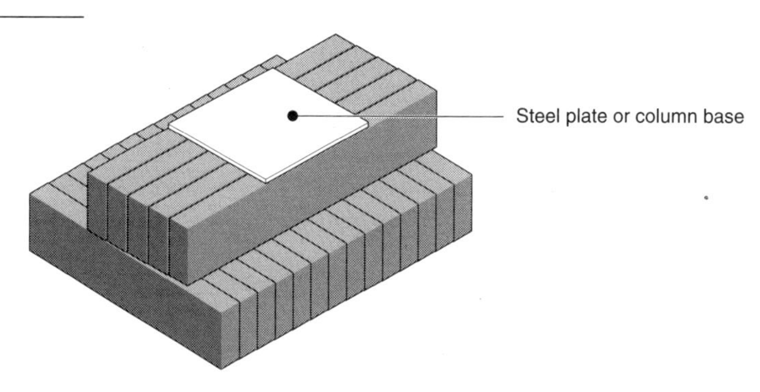

Notes:
1. Except where column extends the full width of the top layer, a 6mm (1/4 in.) thick steel plate shall be located as shown.
2. Top footing members, placed at 90° to the bottom members, shall be long enough to extend over all bottom members.
3. Nails shall be used to fasten securely all members.

Table 5.2
Types of wood column footings

	One storey above foundation		Two storeys above foundation	
Building width (parallel to joist)	Beam span 2.4m (8 ft.)	Beam span 3.0m (10 ft.)	Beam span 2.4m (8 ft.)	Beam span 3.0m (10 ft.)
6.0m (19 ft. - 8 in.)	A	A	B	C
8.0m (26 ft. - 3 in.)	A	B	C	D
10.0m (32 ft. - 9 in.)	B	C	D	D

Notes:
1. Details of the typical footing types designated as A, B, C, and D are provided in Figure 5.8.
2. For beams at end walls, column footing areas may be one-half those shown in Figure 5.8.

Figure 5.8
Types of wood column footings

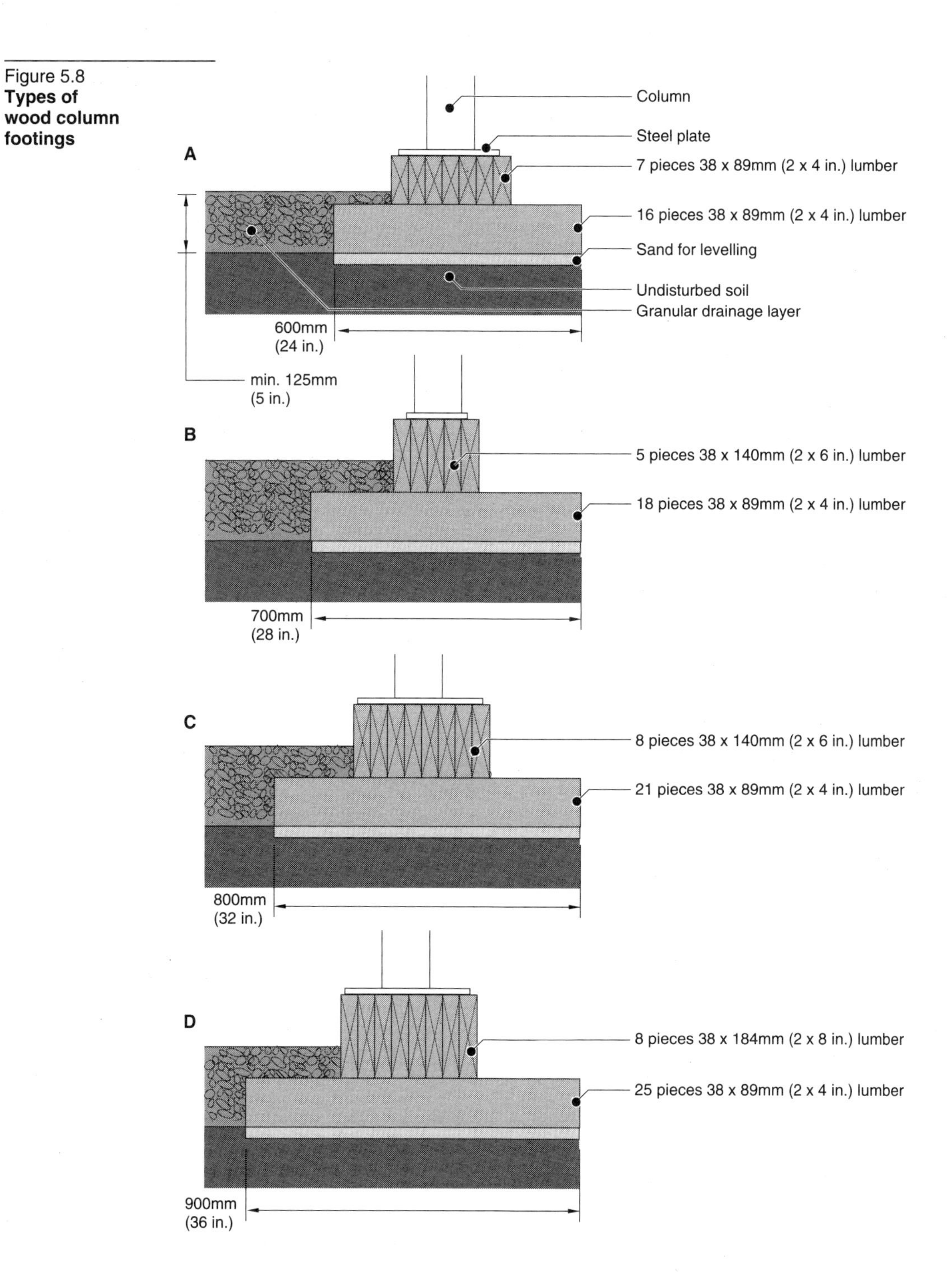

Discontinuous or Stepped Footings

Sloping sites or sites containing bedrock may prevent the use of continuous footings because of the need to locate footings at different elevations. Abrupt changes in footing elevation also occur in certain house designs such as split levels. In these cases discontinuous or stepped footings, made of frames, lintels or concrete, should be used.

Frames

The support frame is made of treated 38 x 140mm (2 x 6 in.) studs sheathed with treated plywood (Figure 5.9). The bottom of the frame rests on an extended portion of the lower foundation footing and its top supports the elevated part of the foundation. The support frame must be thoroughly attached to the main foundation wall and backfilled with crushed gravel.

Lintels

The second method of footing support consists of treated lumber nailed together to form a lintel (Figure 5.10). One end of the lintel is supported by at least one jack stud nailed to the main foundation wall stud. The jack stud rests on an extension to the main foundation footing. The other end of the lintel rests on a footing and compacted gravel, on undisturbed soil, or on a concrete or treated wood column pad that rests on undisturbed soil. Backfill the area below the lintel with crushed gravel.

Concrete

Concrete footings may also be used as stepped footings. Usually the footing steps must run at least 400mm (24 in.) or more before stepping down 400mm or less. This method should be verified with local building officials.

Figure 5.9a **Stepped footing on support frame**

Isometric

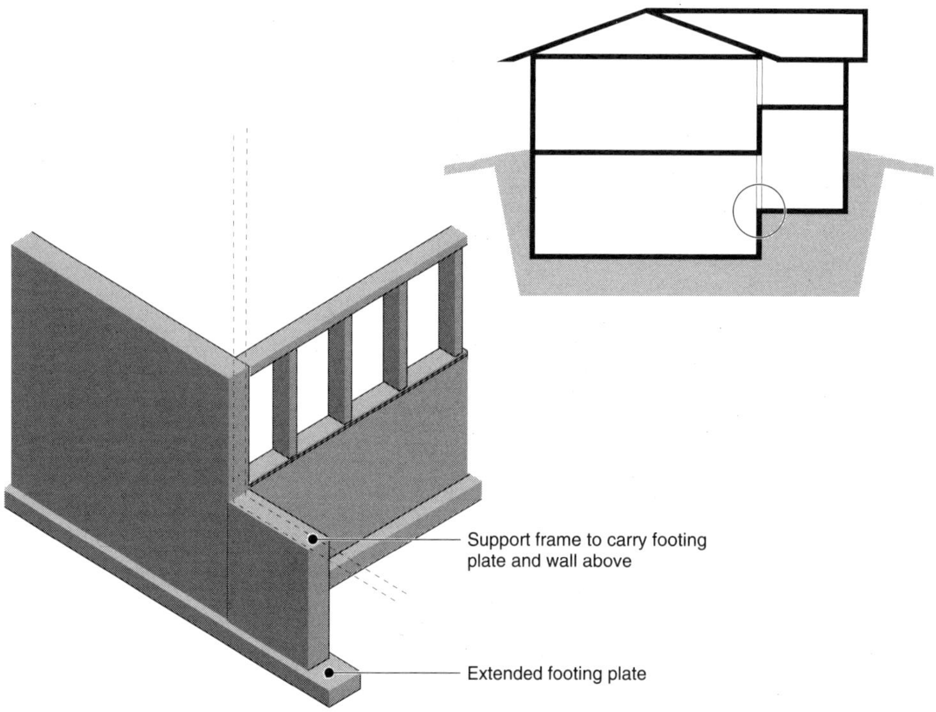

Figure 5.9b
Stepped footing on support frame

Elevation

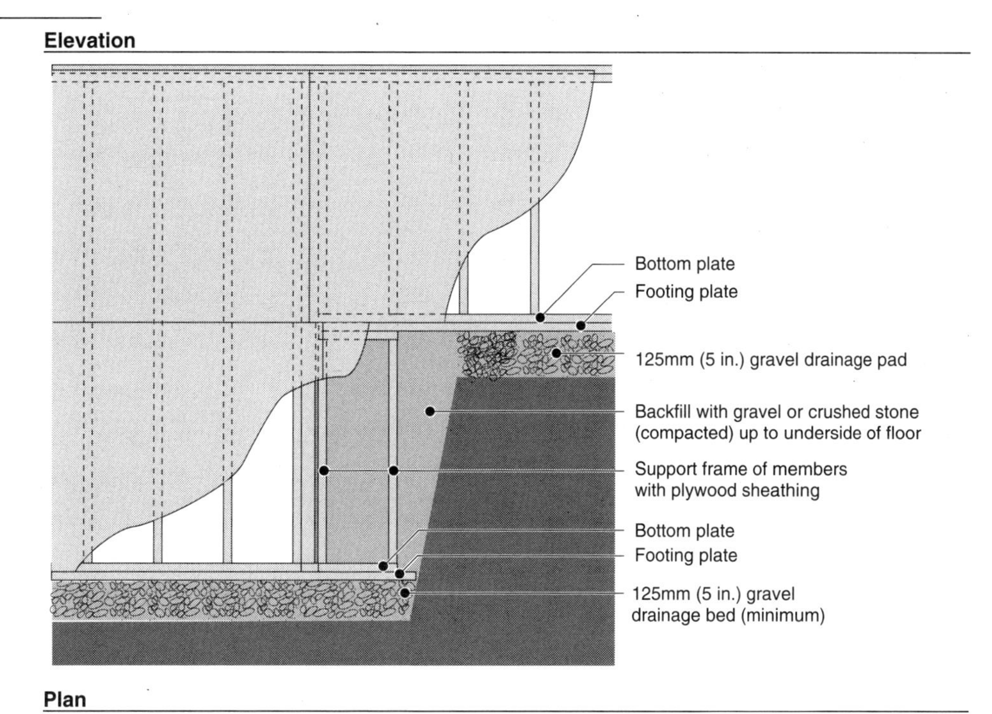

Plan

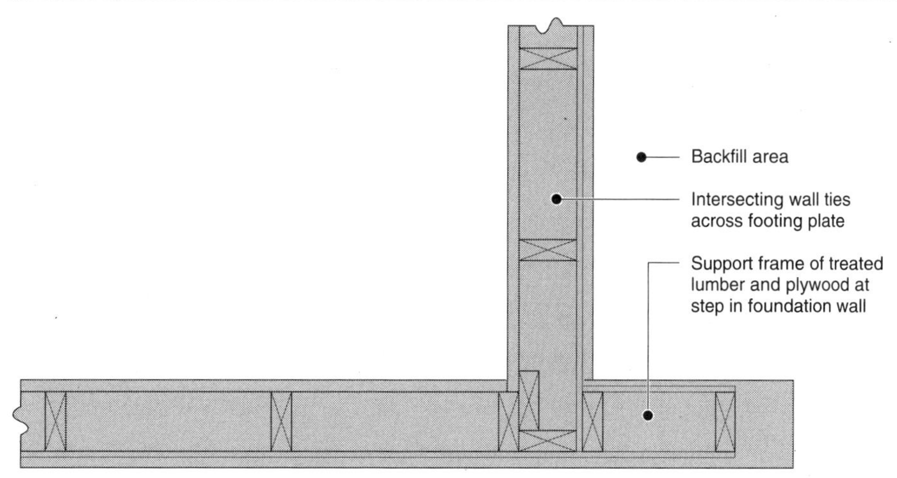

Figure 5.10
Two methods of supporting a stepped footing on a lintel

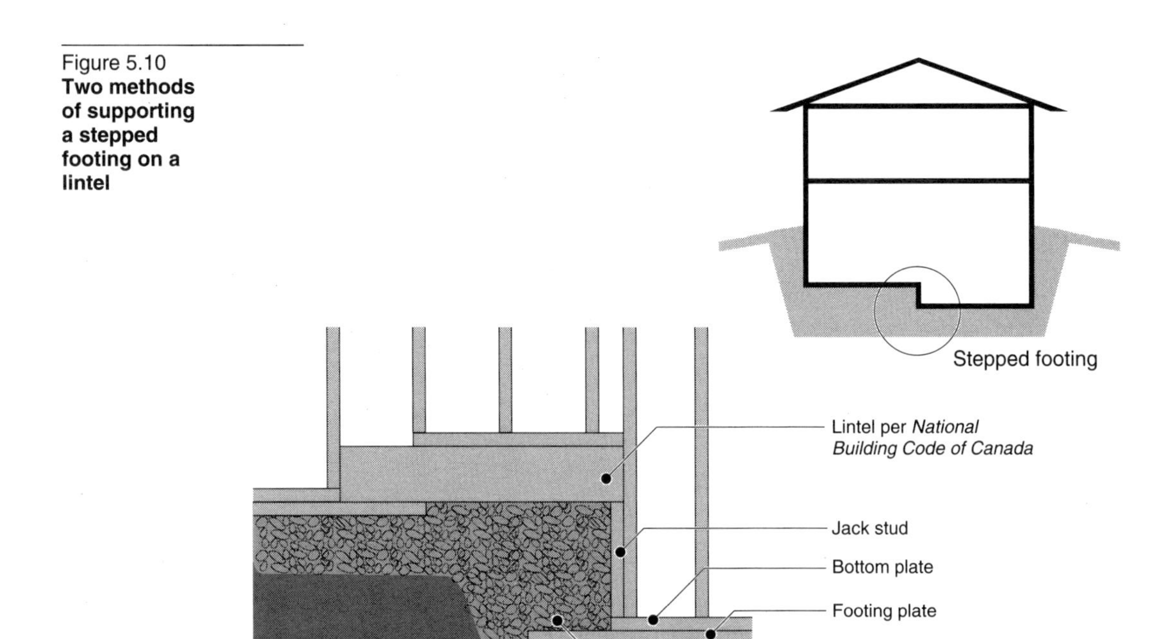

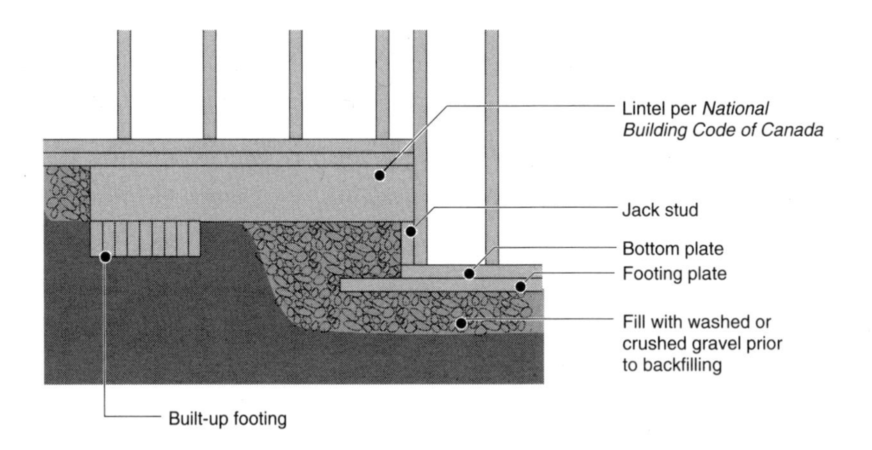

Exterior and Interior Walls

Exterior walls are light-weight and easily handled by framing crews.

6.0 Exterior and Interior Walls

Framing the Walls

Wall Studs

Wood foundation walls can be prefabricated in the shop and erected on site, or completely assembled on site (Figure 6.1). Except at openings, studs are continuous for full basement height of 2.4 to 3m (8 to 10 ft.). For suspended floors, wall studs are 3 to 3.6m (10 to 12 ft.) long since the floor frames into the wall about 600mm (24 in.) above the footing. This method of framing suspended floors into walls is described in Chapter 7.

Figure 6.1
PWF framing

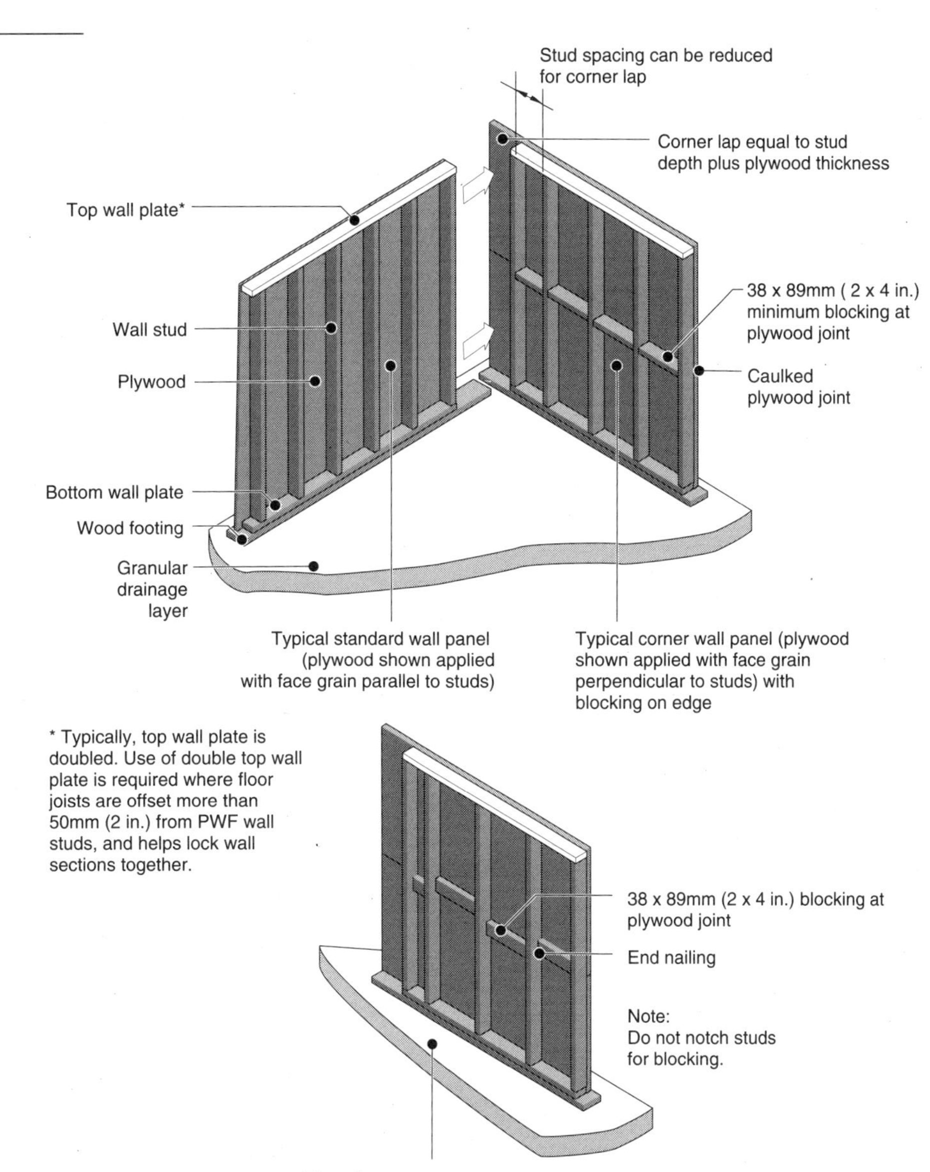

Top Plates

Top and bottom wall plates should be the same width as the studs. Single top wall plates are adequate where ground floor joists will not be offset more than 50mm (2 in.) to one side of the foundation wall studs; however, double top plates are preferred for ease of construction and to fasten adjacent wall sections together.

Where single top plates are used, joints must be located over the studs and reinforced with galvanized steel straps nailed with at least three 63mm (2-1/2 in.) nails on each side of the joint. The straps should be 75mm (3 in.) wide, 150mm (6 in.) long and 0.91mm (1/32 in.) thick.

Table 6.1a
Minimum fastening requirements

	Construction detail		Min. length of nails, mm (in.)	Minimum number or maximum spacing of fasteners
Foundation wall framing (nails)	Bottom wall plate to wood footing plate			
	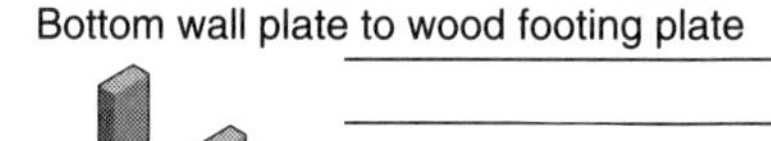		76 (3)	600mm (24 in.) centres
	Bottom wall plate to wall stud			
	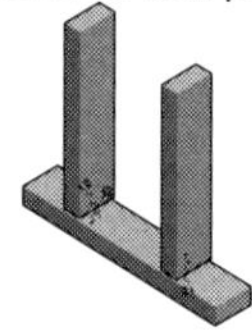	(end nail)	76 (3)	2 each stud
		(toe nail)	63 (2-1/2)	3 each stud
	Top wall plate to stud (end nail)			
		38 x 89mm (2 x 4 in.) stud	89 (3-1/2)	2 each stud
		38 x 140mm (2 x 6 in.) stud	89 (3-1/2)	3 each stud
		38 x 184mm (2 x 8 in.) stud	89 (3-1/2)	4 each stud
	Plate to plate nailing for doubled top plates			
	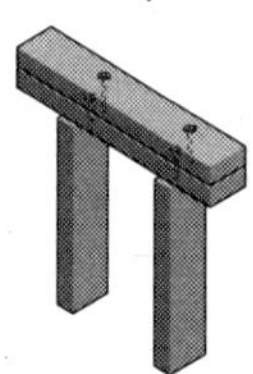	38 x 89mm (2 x 4 in.) stud	76 (3)	2 each stud
		38 x 140mm (2 x 6 in.) stud	76 (3)	3 each stud
		38 x 184mm (2 x 8 in.) stud	76 (3)	4 each stud
	Horizontal wall blocking to wall stud			
			76 (3)	2 each end of each block

Table 6.1b
Minimum fastening requirements

	Construction detail	Min. length of nails, mm (in.)	Minimum number or maximum spacing of fasteners
Floor framing (nails)	End wall reinforcing joists (38 x 89mm (2 x 4 in.)) to floor joists (See Figure 7.6)	76 (3)	400mm (16 in.) centres
	Full depth end wall blocking to floor joists (end nail).(See Detail B, Figure 7.1)	76 (3)	2 each end of each block
	Suspended floors--floor joist to ledger and to top plate of interior bearing support (toe nail).(See Details A and B, Figure 7.3)	76 (3)	2 per joist
	Ledger strip to wall stud. (See Detail A, Figure 7.3)	89 (3-1/2)	3 each stud
Floor attachment to foundation wall (nails and framing straps)	Floor joists and blocking at top of foundation wall to top wall plate (toe nail) (See Figure 7.6)		
	38 x 89mm (2 x 4 in.) wall plate	89 (3-1/2)	2 per joist or per block
	38 x 140mm (2 x 6 in.) wall plate	89 (3-1/2)	3 per joist or per block
	38 x 184mm (2 x 8 in.) wall plate	89 (3-1/2)	4 per joist or per block
	In addition, framing straps are required where backfill height exceeds: (a) 1500mm (5 ft.) with sleeper or slab floor; or (b) 2000mm (6-1/2 ft.) with suspended wood floor (See Figure 7.5)	76 (3)	1 framing strap at every stud with 3 nails into floor header and 3 nails into inner face foundation wall stud
Wall sheathing and subfloor (nails or staples)	Sheathing to wall framing and subfloor to floor joists		
	Nails (See Figure 7.6)	51 (2)	150mm (6 in.) centres along supports
	Staples	51 (2)	100mm (4 in.) centres along edges and 200mm (8 in.) centres along intermediate supports
Framing around windows (framing anchors) (See Figure 6.5)	In addition to normal nailing requirements, framing anchors are required where backfill height exceeds: (a) 1200mm (4 ft.) with sleeper or slab floor; or (b) 2000mm (6-1/2 ft.) with suspended wood floor, at • Sill plate to cripple studs • Sill plate to jack studs	51 (2)	1 framing anchor at each location (see manufacturer's specifications)

Notes:
1. For nailing requirements not covered in this table or the figures use nailing requirements in NBCC.
2. Staples for wood foundations are stainless steel, having a minimum diameter of 1.6mm with a 9.5 crown conforming to American Iron and Steel Institute Inc. 304 or 316.

Where double top plates are used, the upper plate extends the distance of at least two stud spaces from the joint in the lower plate. The upper top plate is usually applied before the wall sections are firmly attached, to facilitate levelling.

Top plates may be untreated if they are located 200mm (8 in.) or more above grade level. Table 6.1 describes the nailing patterns for all framing situations.

Framing Wall Corners

Corners, particularly inside corners, must be adequately framed to resist inward pressure from soil backfill. Figures 6.2, 6.3 and 6.4 provide typical details.

In the inside corner details (Figures 6.3 and 6.4) it is necessary to provide adequate nailing surface between the two intersecting walls to prevent soil pressure from forcing the walls apart.

Figure 6.2 **Framing, outside wall corner**

Isometric

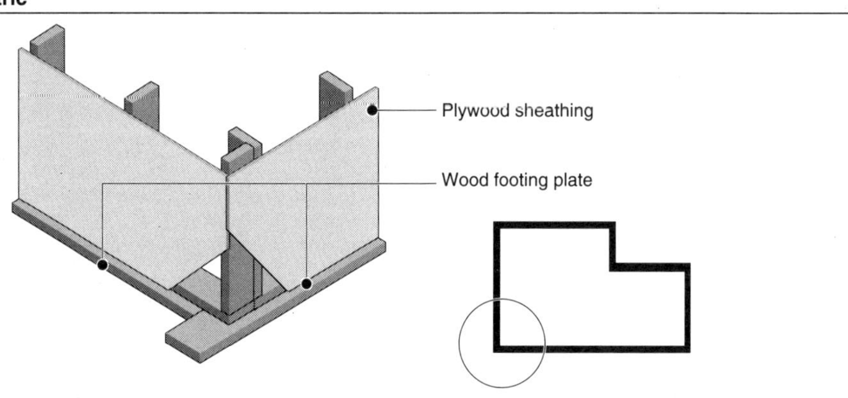

Plan

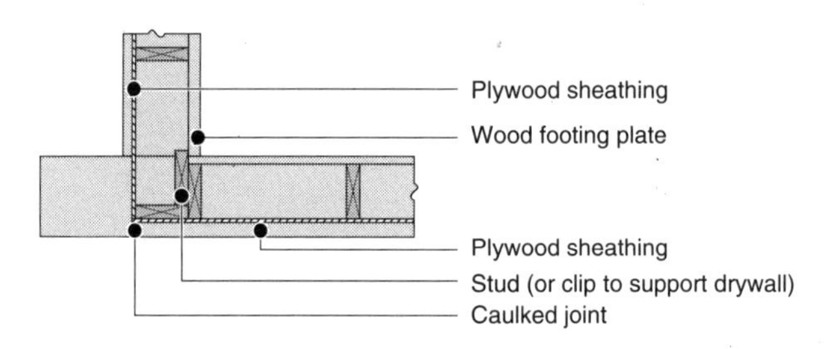

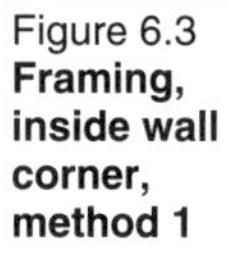

Figure 6.3
Framing, inside wall corner, method 1

Isometric

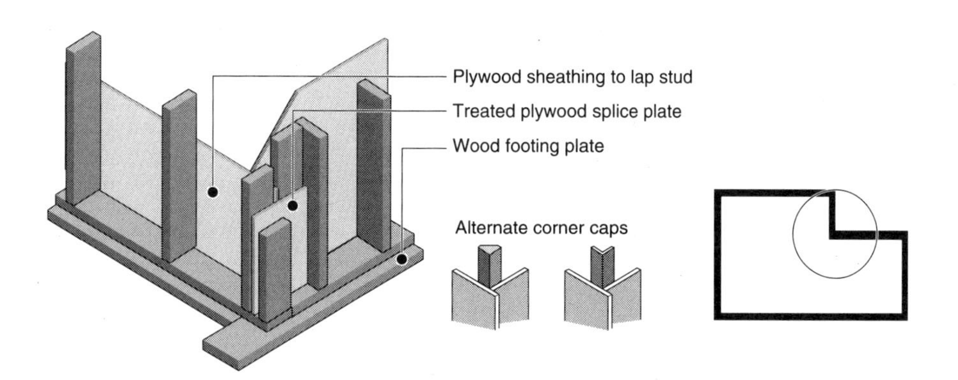

Plan: first stage of assembly

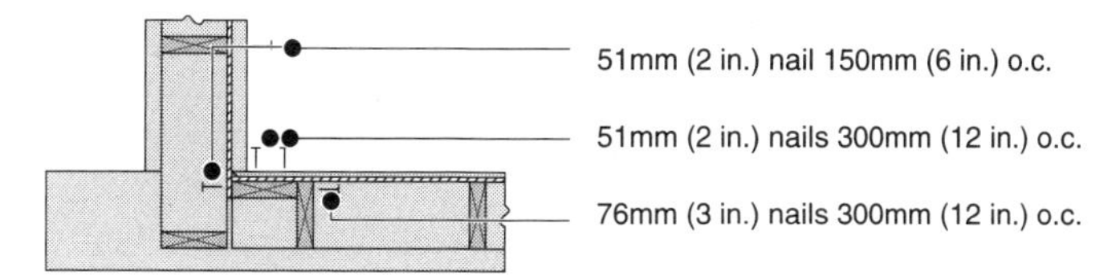

Plan: final stage of assembly

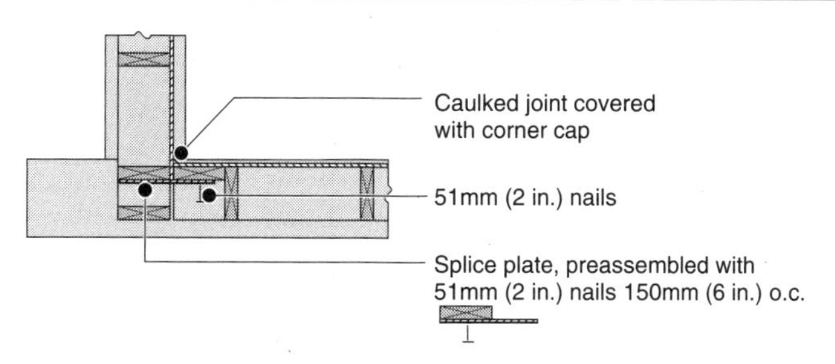

Figure 6.4
Framing, inside wall corner, method 2

Isometric

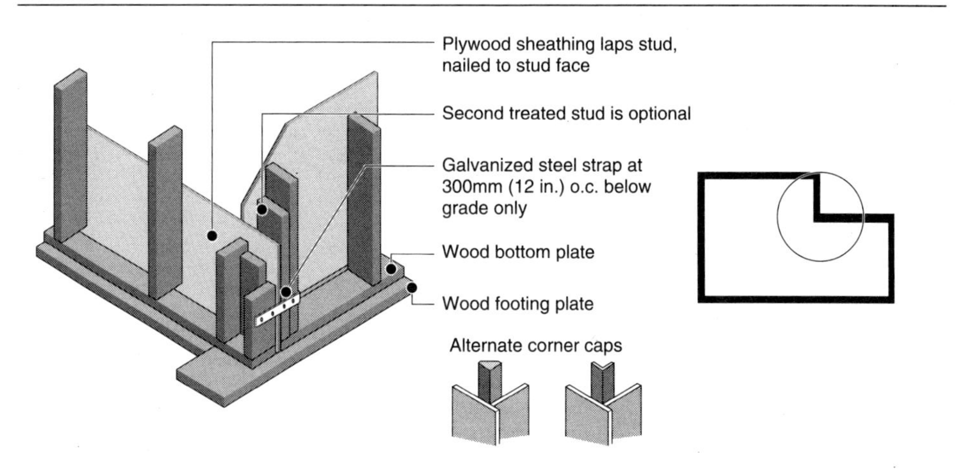

Plan

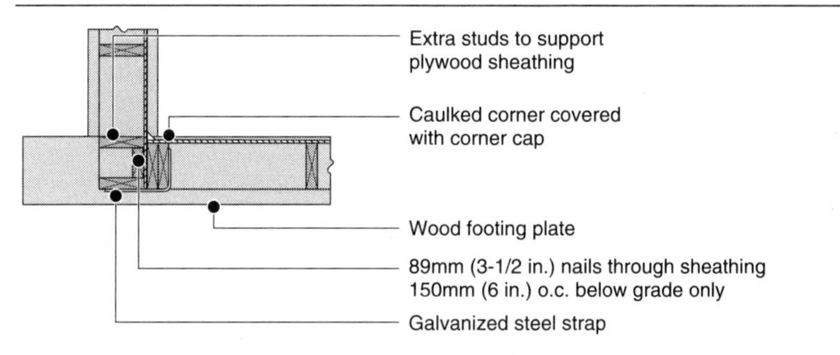

Elevation

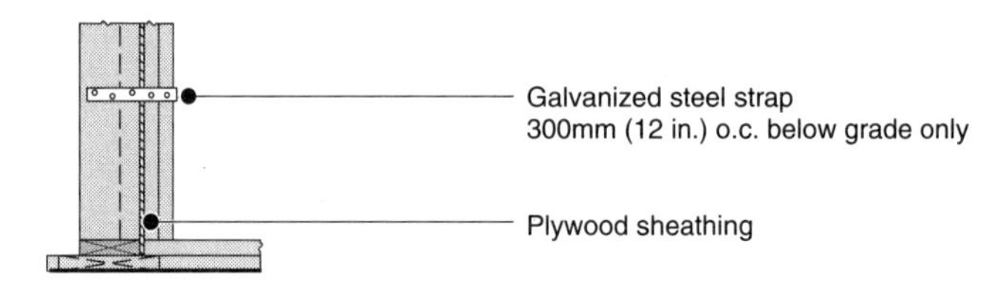

Openings in Foundation Walls

Normal nailing requirements, as described in the building codes, are adequate for window and door openings when:

- PWFs with suspended wood floors have backfill heights of less then 2m (6-1/2 ft.)
- PWFs with wood sleeper or concrete slab floors have backfill heights of less than 1.2m (4 ft.).

When the backfill heights exceed these limits, extra framing and nailing are needed to transfer lateral loads from the window or door opening to the adjacent studs. These requirements are illustrated in Figure 6.5 for window openings and dropped stair landings.

Figure 6.5a
Framing windows and dropped stair landings

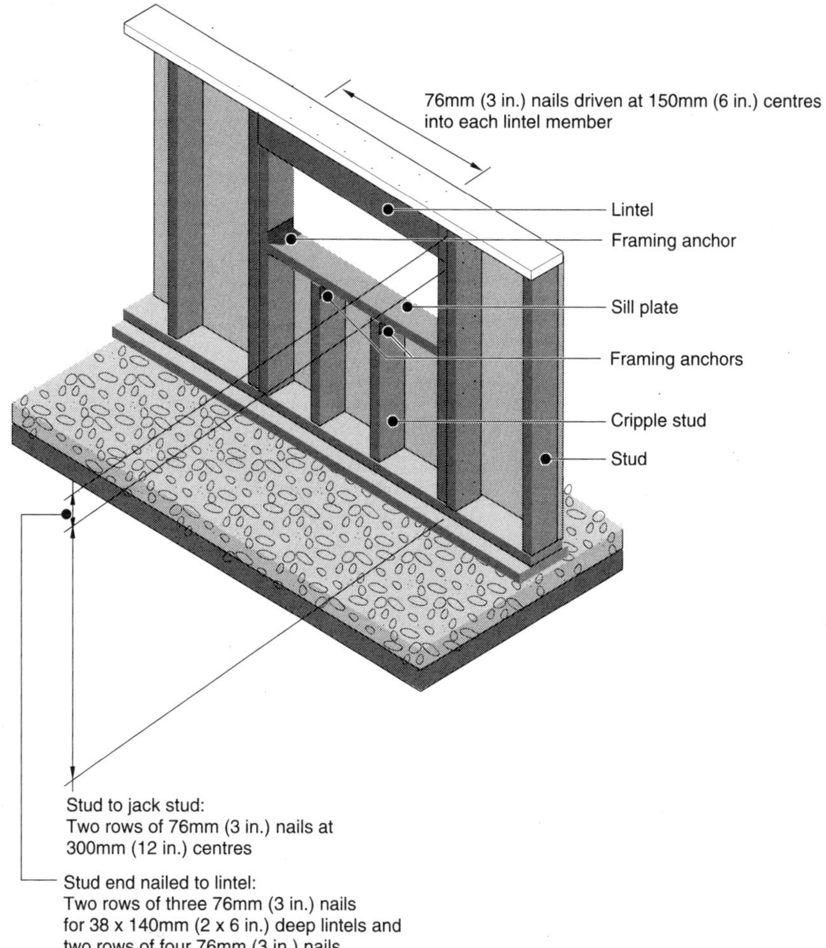

Figure 6.5b
Framing windows and dropped stair landings

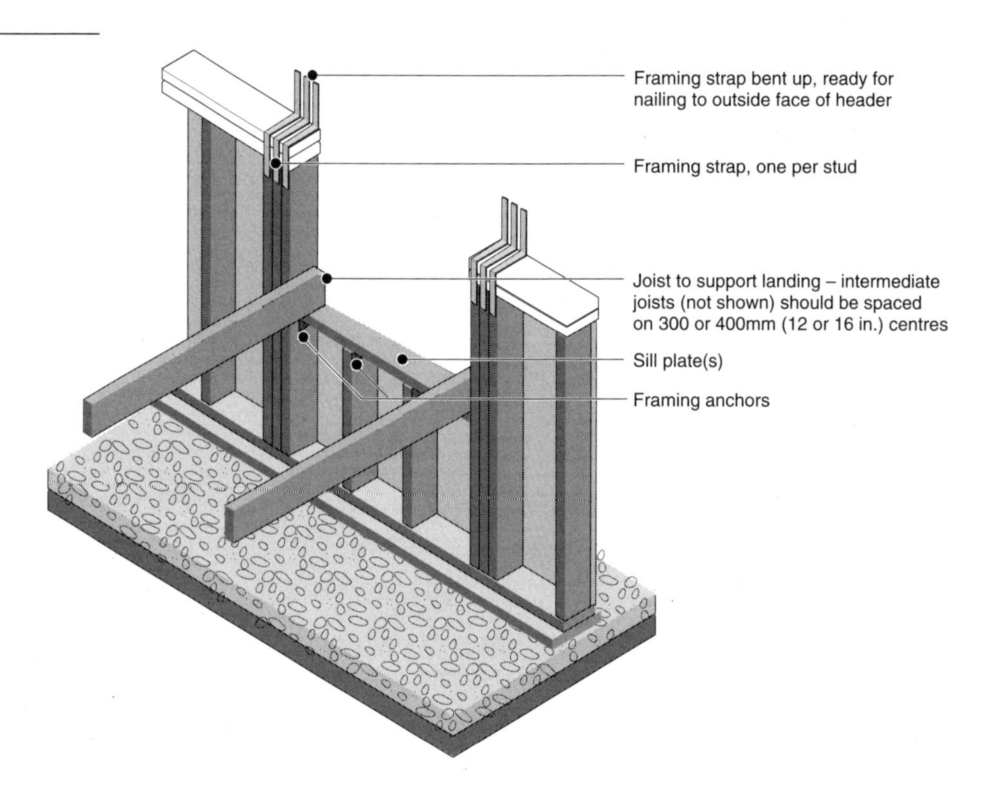

Width of window or landing	Number of studs each side [1]	Number of sill plates [1] for 2.4m (8 ft.) studs	for longer studs
≤ 1.2m (4 ft.)	2	1 - 38 x 140mm (2 x 6 in.)	2 - 38 x 140mm (2 x 6 in.)
≤ 1.8m (6 ft.)	3	2 - 38 x 140mm (2 x 6 in.)	3 - 38 x 140mm (2 x 6 in.)
≤ 2.1m (7 ft.)	3	3 - 38 x 140mm (2 x 6 in.) 2 - 38 x 184mm (2 x 8 in.)	3 - 38 x 184mm (2 x 8 in.)
≤ 2.4m (8 ft.)	4	4 - 38 x 140mm (2 x 6 in.) 3 - 38 x 184mm (2 x 8 in.)	4 - 38 x 184mm (2 x 8 in.)

Notes:
1. Where backfill height is less than 1.2m (4 ft.), the requirements of the local building code apply.

Sheathing

Table 6.2 shows the thickness of plywood sheathing required for various backfill heights. Plywood may be installed vertically, with face grain parallel to the studs, or horizontally, with face grain perpendicular to the studs. The latter method requires more caulked joints but gives a stronger wall, allowing for higher backfill where necessary.

All edges of plywood sheathing panels should be supported by framing, either by the wall studs for vertically applied plywood or by treated 38 x 89mm (2 x 4 in.) blocking between studs for horizontally applied plywood. Plywood sheathing that is entirely more than 200mm (8 in.) above grade need not be treated. Nailing patterns are fully described in Table 6.1.

Table 6.2
Plywood sheathing requirements

Plywood alignment on wall	Stud spacing, mm (in.)	Maximum backfill heights, m (ft.-in.) for plywood thickness		
		12.5mm (1/2 in.)	15.5mm (5/8 in.)	18.5mm (3/4 in.)
Face grain perpendicular to studs	300 (12)	2.9 (9-6)	3.2 (10-6)	3.2 (10-6)
	400 (16)	2.2 (7-3)	2.6 (8-6)	3.2 (10-6)
Face grain parallel to studs	300 (12)	2.1 (6-11)	2.7 (8-10)	3.0 (9-10)
	400 (16)	1.3 (4-3)	2.0 (6-7)	2.2 (7-3)

Notes:
1. Backfill height is the distance from the top of the footing plate to grade level.
2. Plywood thicknesses shown are for unsanded sheathing grade plywood having at least four plies.
3. Four-ply plywood shall be installed with face grain perpendicular to studs.

Caulking the Walls
Caulking between all plywood panel joints helps to prevent the entry of moisture into the foundation.

Apply the caulking in the joints between the plywood panels, and between the bottom of the wall panels and the wood footing. The panel edges should be clean and dry before caulking and if work must proceed in cold weather (less than 5°C), the caulking should be kept within the manufacturers' recommended working temperatures until used.

When the first wall panel is in place, run a bead of caulking along the exposed edge of the plywood. Press the panel edge of the next wall panel into the bead of caulking so that some of the caulking squeezes out of the joint between the two panels. Leave a 2 or 3mm (1/8 in.) gap between wall panels for panel expansion. Caulking may also be applied along the bottom edge of the plywood where it meets the footing.

Where a suspended floor is used, the extra foundation wall height makes a horizontal joint in the plywood wall sheathing necessary. If below grade, this joint is backed by a horizontal blocking member which is the same depth as the stud.

Before backfilling, a moisture barrier is applied. This step is described in Chapter 8, *Moisture Barriers and Backfill.*

Interior Loadbearing Walls

Interior loadbearing walls are constructed in accordance with the requirements of the appropriate building code. These walls are supported on either wood or concrete footings (See Figures 5.2, 5.3, and 5.4), which are similar to those supporting the exterior walls. Figures 6.6 and 6.7 show methods of attaching interior bearing walls to exterior walls.

Figure 6.6
Attachment of interior bearing walls to exterior walls, method 1

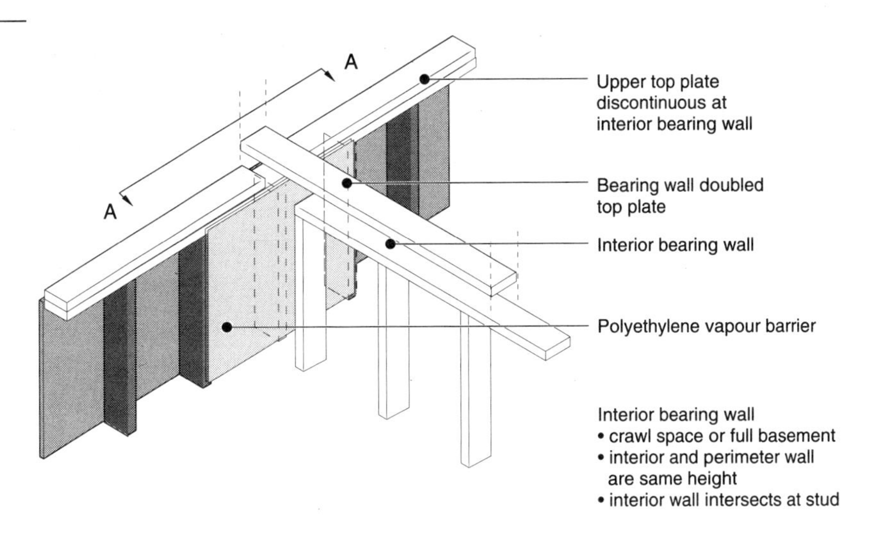

Interior bearing wall
- crawl space or full basement
- interior and perimeter wall are same height
- interior wall intersects at stud

Plan detail: Section AA

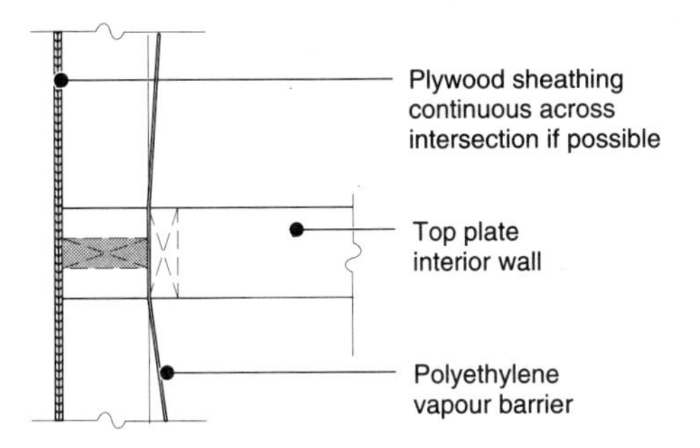

Alternative plan detail: Section AA

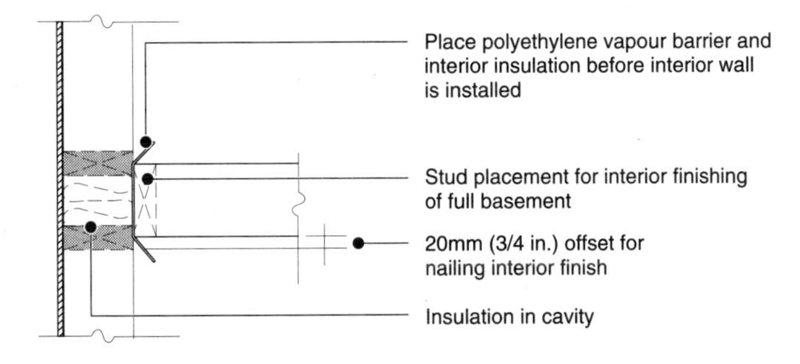

Figure 6.7
Attachment of interior bearing walls to exterior walls, method 2

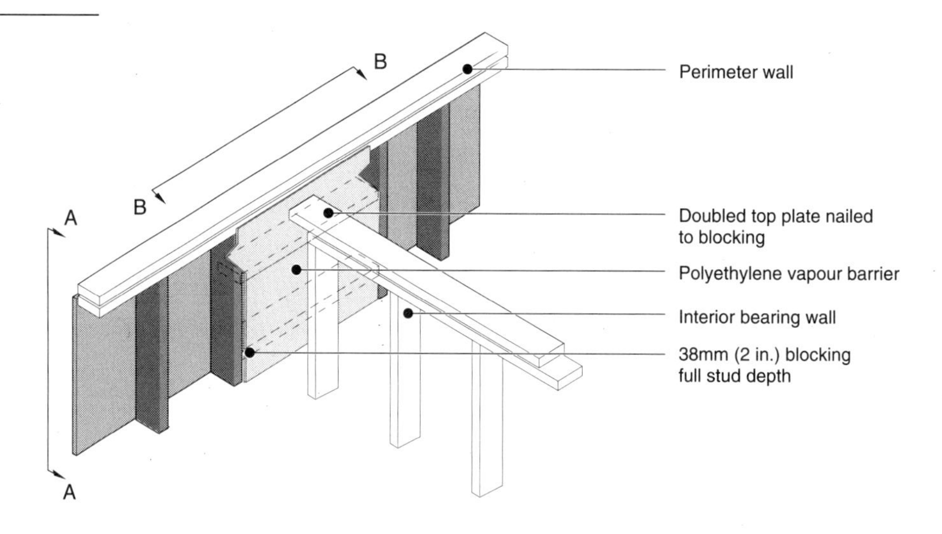

Section AA

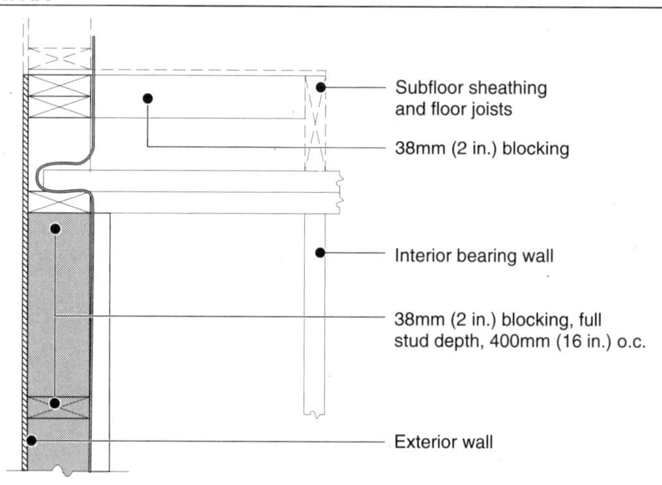

Section BB

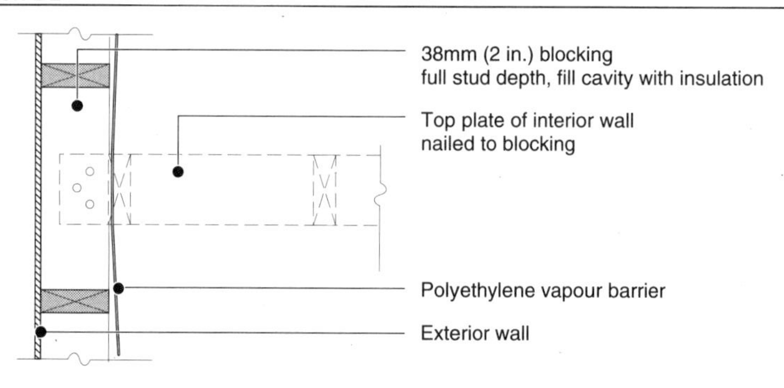

Walls Supporting Brick Veneer

Brick veneer can be supported on either a knee wall or on top of the main foundation wall.

Support on Knee Wall

The knee wall shown in Figure 6.8 is one method of supporting a single wythe of brick veneer up to two stories in height.

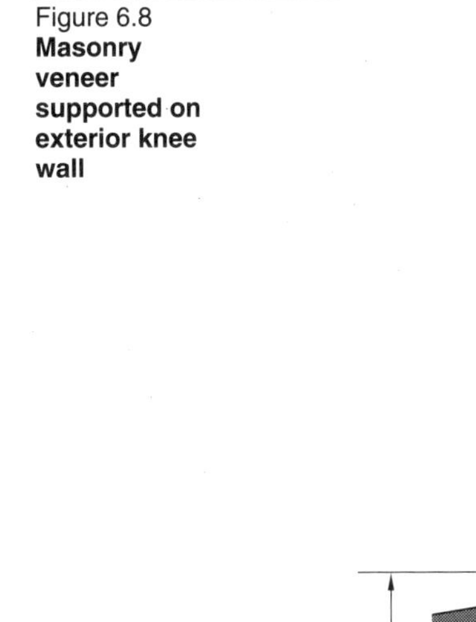

Figure 6.8
Masonry veneer supported on exterior knee wall

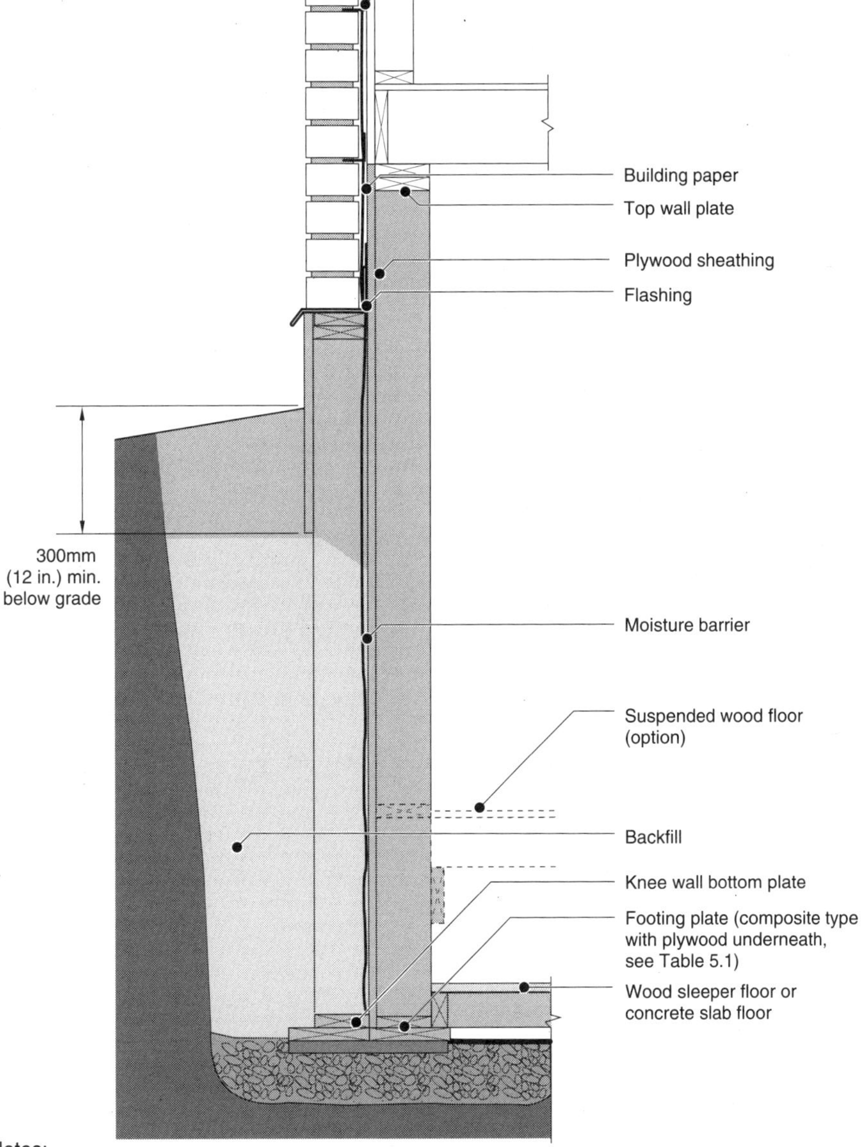

Notes:
1. Knee wall sheathing shall extend to at least 300mm (12 in.) below grade.
2. Backfill may occupy space between knee wall studs.
3. Main foundation wall moisture barrier shall be continuous between exterior wall sheathing and knee wall framing.
4. Moisture barrier shall not extend under the footing plates or between the granular drainage layer and the backfill.

Knee wall studs are usually 38 x 89mm (2 x 4 in.) spaced 400mm (16 in.) o.c. and nailed at the top and bottom of each stud to the main foundation wall after the moisture barrier is in place.

Where knee wall studs are longer than 1500mm (5 ft.) they should be toenailed at midheight to the main foundation wall.

The top plate of the knee wall must be doubled by nailing together two 38 x 89mm (2 x 4 in.) members. Joints in the the upper and lower top plates should be offset a minimum of two stud spacings from one another and occur directly over a knee wall stud.

Knee wall sheathing extends downwards from the top of the knee wall to a minimum of 300mm (12 in.) below grade. Sheathing is not required below this point, simply backfill between the exposed knee wall studs.

Support on Main Foundation Wall

Where brick veneer is supported on top of the foundation wall, double top plates must be wide enough to provide adequate support for the brick as well as the floor framing (Figure 6.9). The double top plate is built of pressure treated lumber. Install and anchor the brick according to the national or provincial building codes.

The weight of the brick must be considered in the selection of stud size (see footnote 3 to Table 6.4).

Figure 6.9 **Masonry veneer supported on main wall**

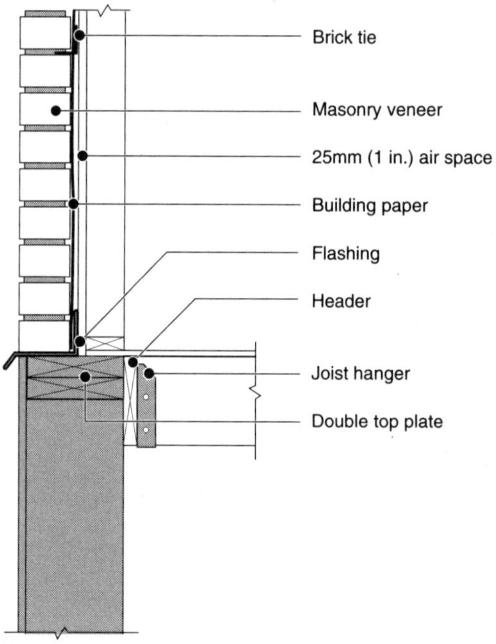

Brick tie
Masonry veneer
25mm (1 in.) air space
Building paper
Flashing
Header
Joist hanger
Double top plate

Wall Construction When Backfill Height is Not Uniform

Normal framing and nailing methods allow floors and walls to perform adequately as shearwalls and diaphragms. Diaphragms (floors) and shearwalls transmit loads in their own planes to keep buildings square.

In practice, side walls distribute backfill or wind loads to the floor, which in turn transfers loads to the end walls (Figure 6.10). It is only in special situations, such as with long, narrow buildings or with unequal backfill heights, that floors and walls must be checked for their shearwall and diaphragm capacity, and extra nailing added as required.

There are also conditions, such as building on loose sand or filled ground or in areas with excessive hydrostatic pressure or wind, that could lead to deformation. In these conditions an engineer should be consulted.

Where backfill heights differ by more than 600mm (2 ft.) on opposite (side) walls of a foundation, racking loads are exerted at the edges of the panels. This occurs most often in buildings on the sides of hills, or in homes with full walk-out basements where there is high backfill on one side and little or no counter-balancing backfill on the other.

Under these conditions, the foundation must be strengthened by extra nailing of the sheathing to the end wall, or by other means, such as interior shearwalls. Table 6.3 gives guidance on end wall nailing. See Chapter 10 for further details on walk-out basements.

Figure 6.10
The effect of unequal backfill heights

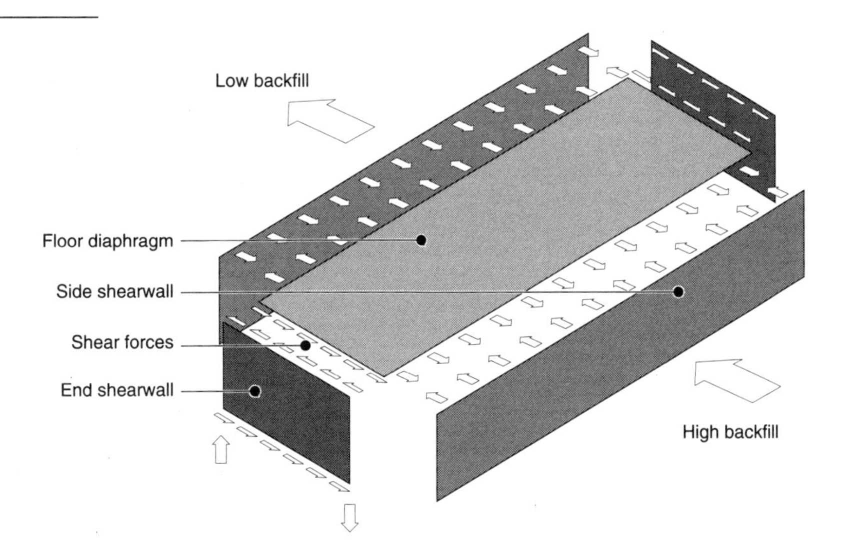

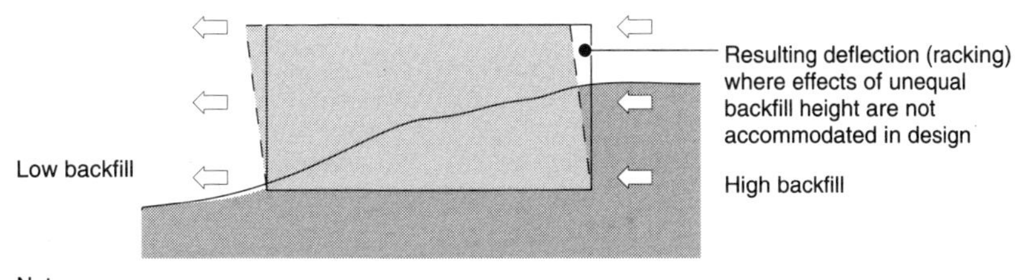

Note:
Decreasing nail spacing around perimeter of end shearwall will help to prevent racking. See table 6.5.

Table 6.3a
Perimeter nail spacings for differential backfill heights

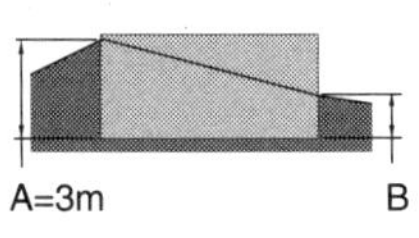

Backfill A = 3m	Perimeter nail spacings, (mm)					
	L/W = 0.4		L/W = 0.6		L/W = 0.8	
	Nail length		Nail length		Nail length	
Backfill B (m)	63mm	76mm	63mm	76mm	63mm	76mm
0 to 0.9	100	100	65	65	50	65
1.0 to 1.5	100	150	65	100	50	65
1.51 to 1.8	100	150	65	100	65	65
1.81 to 2.1	150	150	100	100	65	65
2.2 to 2.4	150	150	100	100	65	100
2.5 or higher	150	150	150	150	150	150

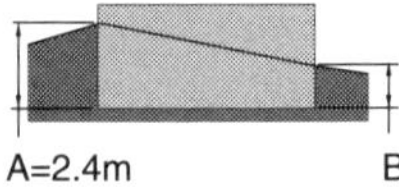

Backfill A = 2.4m	Perimeter nail spacings, (mm)					
	L/W = 0.6		L/W = 1.0		L/W = 1.4	
	Nail length		Nail length		Nail length	
Backfill B (m)	63mm	76mm	63mm	76mm	63mm	76mm
0 to 0.6	100	100	65	100	65	65
0.61 to 1.2	100	150	65	100	65	65
1.21 to 1.5	100	150	100	100	65	65
1.51 to 1.81	150	150	100	150	65	100
1.81 or higher	150	150	150	150	150	150

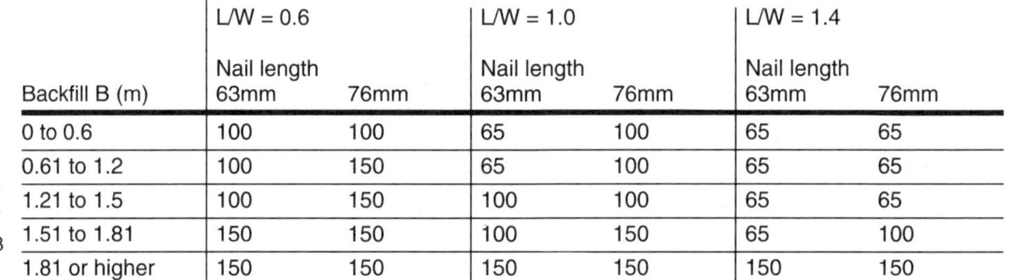

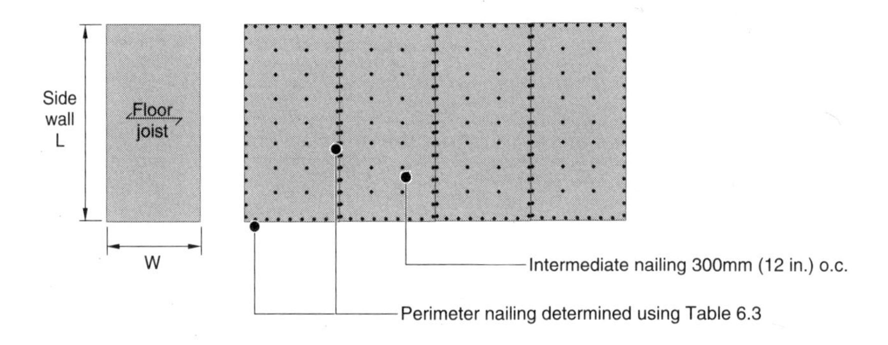

Table 6.3b
Perimeter nail spacings for differential backfill heights

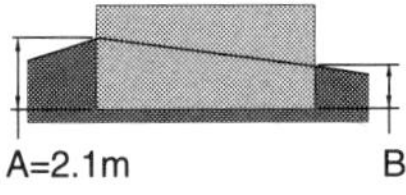

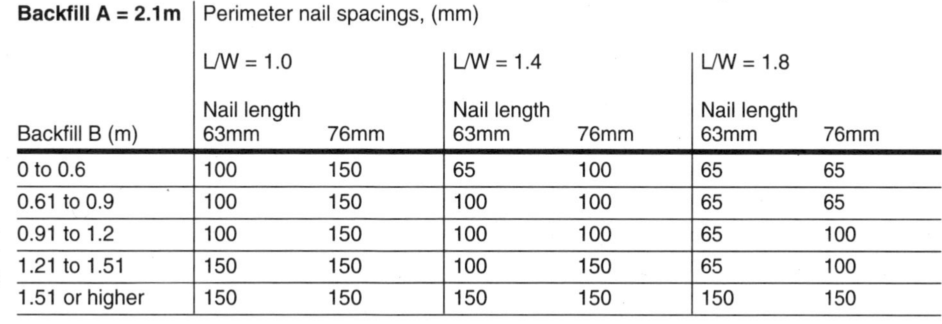

Backfill A = 2.1m	Perimeter nail spacings, (mm)					
	L/W = 1.0		L/W = 1.4		L/W = 1.8	
	Nail length		Nail length		Nail length	
Backfill B (m)	63mm	76mm	63mm	76mm	63mm	76mm
0 to 0.6	100	150	65	100	65	65
0.61 to 0.9	100	150	100	100	65	65
0.91 to 1.2	100	150	100	100	65	100
1.21 to 1.51	150	150	100	150	65	100
1.51 or higher	150	150	150	150	150	150

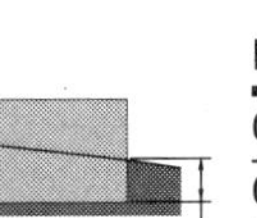

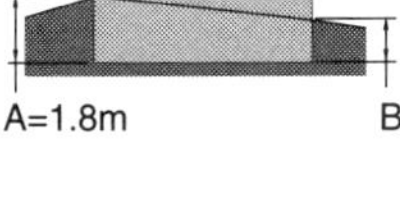

Backfill A = 1.8m	Perimeter nail spacings, (mm)					
	L/W = 1.6		L/W = 2.0		L/W = 2.5	
	Nail length		Nail length		Nail length	
Backfill B (m)	63mm	76mm	63mm	76mm	63mm	76mm
0 to 0.9	100	150	100	100	65	100
0.91 to 1.20	150	150	100	150	100	100
1.21 or higher	150	150	150	150	150	150

A=1.5m B

Backfill A = 1.5m	Perimeter nail spacings, (mm)					
	L/W = 2.0		L/W = 2.5		L/W = 3.0	
	Nail length		Nail length		Nail length	
Backfill B (m)	63mm	76mm	63mm	76mm	63mm	76mm
0 to 0.9	150	150	150	150	100	150
0.91 or higher	150	150	150	150	150	150

Notes:
1. This table appears in the Appendix in Imperial units.
2. All panel edges backed with pressure treated 38 x 89mm (2 x 4 in.) framing or wider. Sheathing installed either horizontally or vertically. Space nails at 300mm (12 in.) on centre along intermediate studs.
3. For L/W ratios less than the lowest ratios listed, the nail spacings shown for the lowest ratios may be used.

Buildings longer than 15m (50 ft.), having a length to width ratio greater than 4:1 may be subject to loading conditions that exceed those covered in Table 6.3. These buildings should be checked by an engineer for adequate shearwall action.

Interior Shearwalls

Another way of improving the shearwall capacity of long, narrow foundations, defined as longer than 15m (50 ft.), or with a length to width ratio greater than 4:1, is by designing interior basement partitions to act as shearwalls.

Strength of the shearwall is determined mainly by the amount of nailing of plywood or oriented strand board (OSB) sheathing to the framing members. Joints between plywood or OSB panel sheets should be staggered and blocking for plywood or OSB edges installed at mid-wall height. Framing around openings in shearwalls should be sufficient to transfer shear forces.

Like other interior loadbearing walls, interior shearwall partitions can rest directly on a concrete or wood footing, or on the foundation floor in which case they can be constructed of untreated wood. They must be anchored to the floor and to the side walls.

The top of the wall is fastened to the overhead floor joists by nailing blocking on the flat between joists that run parallel to the shearwall (Figure 6.11). In this case, the ceiling should be nailed to the blocking. Where floor joists run perpendicular to the shearwall, install the blocking between the joists and fasten the shearwall to the blocking with framing clips (Figure 6.11).

Interior shearwalls should be installed before nailing on the first floor subfloor and before backfilling.

Figure 6.11
Fastening interior shearwalls

Parallel to floor joists

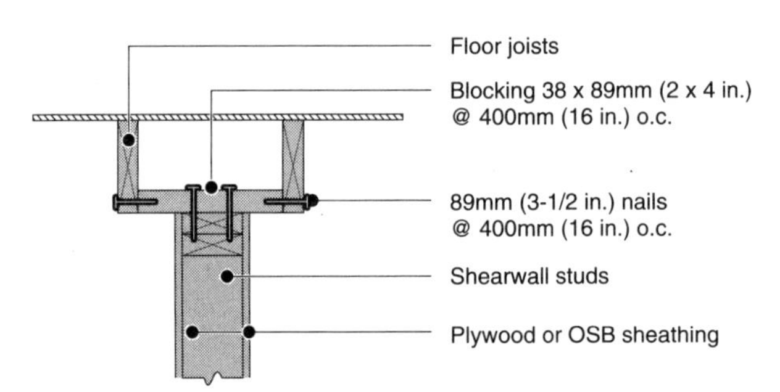

Perpendicular to floor joists

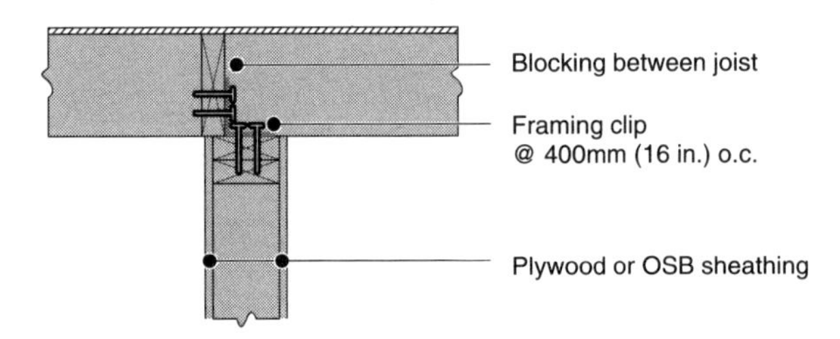

Stud Wall Selection Tables

Before building the walls it is necessary to determine stud size and spacing and thickness of plywood, all of which depend on the magnitude of the loads the walls must resist. The magnitude of vertical loads acting on the foundation walls depends on the number of storeys, the area of the building and the geographic location (for snow loads). Lateral loads on walls vary with the height of backfill and soil type.

Stud size and spacing for a given backfill height are determined using Table 6.4 and the Stud Wall Selection Tables as explained in the following example.

Example

You wish to build a house that has the following characteristics: centre support (floor beam), one storey with brick veneer supported on the main foundation wall, 8.5m wide (length of end wall), roof snow load of 2 kN/m^2 and wood sleeper floor.

Step 1

Go to Table 6.4 to determine the vertical load the foundation must support. The vertical load is 22 kN/m plus 4 kN/m for one storey of brick veneer for a total vertical load of 26 kN/m.

Step 2

Go to the "Wood Sleeper and Slab on Grade" stud wall selection tables. Knowing the vertical load, you have choice of stud size, species and stud spacing. If you need a 1.5 m (5 ft.) backfill height using No.2 grade, species group 1 (e.g., lodgepole pine or jack pine) lumber, the stud size for a vertical load of 26 kN/m, with studs spaced 400mm (16 in.) o.c., is 38 x 140mm (2 x 6 in.).

Spacing the studs 300mm (12 in.) o.c. allows for a backfill height of 1.8m (6 ft.).

Table 6.4
Factored vertical loads on PWF walls, kN/m

	Case 1: No centre floor supports					
	1 Storey			2 Storeys		
Specified roof load (kPa)	House width, m (ft.-in.) 5 (16-5)	6.5 (21-4)	8 (26-3)	House width, m (ft.-in.) 5 (16-5)	6.5 (21-4)	8 (26-3)
1.0	14	17	21	21	26	31
1.5	16	20	24	22	28	34
2.0	18	22	26	24	30	36
2.5	19	24	29	26	33	39
3.0	21	27	32	28	35	42

	Case 2: With centre floor supports					
	1 Storey			2 Storeys		
Specified roof load (kPa)	House width, m (ft.-in.) 7 (23-0)	8.5 (27-11)	10 (32-10)	House width, m (ft.-in.) 7 (23-0)	8.5 (27-11)	10 (32-10)
1.0	13	16	18	19	22	25
1.5	16	19	22	21	25	28
2.0	18	22	25	23	28	32
2.5	21	25	28	26	31	35
3.0	23	28	32	28	33	39

Notes:
1. Vertical load is expressed in units of load (kN) per unit of wall length (m).
2. Table 6.4 and the Stud Wall Selection Tables apply to residential loads only, not to commercial loads.
3. For brick veneer supported on main foundation wall, add 4 kN/m per storey of veneer.
4. Specified roof load for a given geographic area is found in building codes or through local government building authorities.

PWF Stud Selection Tables

2.4m 400mm

Wood Sleeper or Slab on Grade

Stud length = 2.4m (8 ft.)
Stud spacing = 400mm (16 in.)

Vertical load range kN/m (plf)	Species	Grade	Backfill height, m (ft.-in.) 1.2 (4-0)	1.4 (4-6)	1.5 (5-0)	1.7 (5-6)	1.8 (6-0)	2 (6-6)	2.1 (7-0)	2.3 (7-6)
15 (1030)	Group 1	Sel Str	6	6	6	6	6	6	8	8
to	Group 1	No. 1/No. 2	6	6	6	8	8	8	10	10
20 (1370)	Group 2	Sel Str	6	6	6	8	8	8	10	10
	Group 2	No. 1/No. 2	6	6	8	8	10	10	10	n/a
20.1 (1375)	Group 1	Sel Str	6	6	6	6	6	6	8	8
to	Group 1	No. 1/No. 2	6	6	6	8	8	8	10	10
25 (1715)	Group 2	Sel Str	6	6	6	8	8	8	10	10
	Group 2	No. 1/No. 2	6	6	8	8	10	10	10	n/a
25.1 (1720)	Group 1	Sel Str	6	6	6	6	6	8	8	8
to	Group 1	No. 1/No. 2	6	6	6	8	8	8	10	10
30 (2055)	Group 2	Sel Str	6	6	6	8	8	8	10	10
	Group 2	No. 1/No. 2	6	8	8	8	10	10	n/a	n/a
30.1 (2060)	Group 1	Sel Str	6	6	6	6	6	8	8	8
to	Group 1	No. 1/No. 2	6	6	6	8	8	10	10	10
35 (2400)	Group 2	Sel Str	6	6	6	8	8	10	10	10
	Group 2	No. 1/No. 2	6	8	8	10	10	10	n/a	n/a
35.1 (2405)	Group 1	Sel Str	6	6	6	6	6	8	8	8
to	Group 1	No. 1/No. 2	6	6	8	8	8	10	10	10
40 (2740)	Group 2	Sel Str	6	6	8	8	8	10	10	10
	Group 2	No. 1/No. 2	6	8	8	10	10	10	n/a	n/a
40.1 (2750)	Group 1	Sel Str	6	6	6	6	8	8	8	8
to	Group 1	No. 1/No. 2	6	6	8	8	8	10	10	10
45 (3085)	Group 2	Sel Str	6	6	8	8	8	10	10	10
	Group 2	No. 1/No. 2	8	8	8	10	10	10	n/a	n/a
45.1 (3090)	Group 1	Sel Str	6	6	6	6	8	8	8	8
to	Group 1	No. 1/No. 2	6	6	8	8	8	10	10	10
50 (3425)	Group 2	Sel Str	6	6	8	8	8	10	10	10
	Group 2	No. 1/No. 2	8	8	8	10	10	10	n/a	n/a

Notes:
1. 4 is a 38 x 89mm stud (2 x 4 in.)
2. 6 is a 38 x 140mm stud (2 x 6 in.)
3. 8 is a 38 x 184mm stud (2 x 8 in.)
4. 10 is a 38 x 235mm stud (2 x 10 in.)
5. Species Group 1 is S-P-F, D.Fir-L, Hem-Fir
6. Species Group 2 is Northern Species Group
7. Tabulated sizes were calculated using Imperial dimensions for stud length, stud spacing and backfill height.

PWF Stud Selection Tables

Wood Sleeper or Slab on Grade

2.4m 300mm

Vertical load range kN/m (plf)	Species	Grade	Stud length = 2.4m (8 ft.) Stud spacing = 300mm (12 in.) Backfill height, m (ft.-in.)							
			1.2 (4-0)	1.4 (4-6)	1.5 (5-0)	1.7 (5-6)	1.8 (6-0)	2 (6-6)	2.1 (7-0)	2.3 (7-6)
15 (1030)	Group 1	Sel Str	4	6	6	6	6	6	6	6
to	Group 1	No. 1/No. 2	4	6	6	6	6	8	8	8
20 (1370)	Group 2	Sel Str	6	6	6	6	6	8	8	8
	Group 2	No. 1/No. 2	6	6	6	8	8	8	10	10
20.1 (1375)	Group 1	Sel Str	4	6	6	6	6	6	6	6
to	Group 1	No. 1/No. 2	6	6	6	6	6	8	8	8
25 (1715)	Group 2	Sel Str	6	6	6	6	6	8	8	8
	Group 2	No. 1/No. 2	6	6	6	8	8	8	10	10
25.1 (1720)	Group 1	Sel Str	4	6	6	6	6	6	6	6
to	Group 1	No. 1/No. 2	6	6	6	6	6	8	8	8
30 (2055)	Group 2	Sel Str	6	6	6	6	6	8	8	8
	Group 2	No. 1/No. 2	6	6	6	8	8	8	10	10
30.1 (2060)	Group 1	Sel Str	4	6	6	6	6	6	6	6
to	Group 1	No. 1/No. 2	6	6	6	6	8	8	8	8
35 (2400)	Group 2	Sel Str	6	6	6	6	8	8	8	8
	Group 2	No. 1/No. 2	6	6	6	8	8	10	10	10
35.1 (2405)	Group 1	Sel Str	6	6	6	6	6	6	6	8
to	Group 1	No. 1/No. 2	6	6	6	6	8	8	8	10
40 (2740)	Group 2	Sel Str	6	6	6	6	8	8	8	8
	Group 2	No. 1/No. 2	6	6	8	8	8	10	10	10
40.1 (2750)	Group 1	Sel Str	6	6	6	6	6	6	6	8
to	Group 1	No. 1/No. 2	6	6	6	6	8	8	8	10
45 (3085)	Group 2	Sel Str	6	6	6	6	8	8	8	10
	Group 2	No. 1/No. 2	6	6	8	8	8	10	10	10
45.1 (3090)	Group 1	Sel Str	6	6	6	6	6	6	6	8
to	Group 1	No. 1/No. 2	6	6	6	6	8	8	8	10
50 (3425)	Group 2	Sel Str	6	6	6	6	8	8	8	10
	Group 2	No. 1/No. 2	6	6	8	8	8	10	10	10

Notes:
1. 4 is a 38 x 89mm stud (2 x 4 in.)
2. 6 is a 38 x 140mm stud (2 x 6 in.)
3. 8 is a 38 x 184mm stud (2 x 8 in.)
4. 10 is a 38 x 235mm stud (2 x 10 in.)
5. Species Group 1 is S-P-F, D.Fir-L, Hem-Fir
6. Species Group 2 is Northern Species Group
7. Tabulated sizes were calculated using Imperial dimensions for stud length, stud spacing and backfill height.

PWF Stud Selection Tables

2.4m 200mm

Wood Sleeper or Slab on Grade

Stud length = 2.4m (8 ft.)
Stud spacing = 200mm (8 in.)

Vertical load range kN/m (plf)	Species	Grade	Backfill height, m (ft.-in.) 1.2 (4-0)	1.4 (4-6)	1.5 (5-0)	1.7 (5-6)	1.8 (6-0)	2 (6-6)	2.1 (7-0)	2.3 (7-6)
15 (1030)	Group 1	Sel Str	4	4	4	6	6	6	6	6
to	Group 1	No. 1/No. 2	4	4	6	6	6	6	6	6
20 (1370)	Group 2	Sel Str	4	4	6	6	6	6	6	6
	Group 2	No. 1/No. 2	4	6	6	6	6	6	8	8
20.1 (1375)	Group 1	Sel Str	4	4	4	6	6	6	6	6
to	Group 1	No. 1/No. 2	4	4	6	6	6	6	6	6
25 (1715)	Group 2	Sel Str	4	4	6	6	6	6	6	6
	Group 2	No. 1/No. 2	4	6	6	6	6	6	8	8
25.1 (1720)	Group 1	Sel Str	4	4	4	6	6	6	6	6
to	Group 1	No. 1/No. 2	4	4	6	6	6	6	6	6
30 (2055)	Group 2	Sel Str	4	4	6	6	6	6	6	6
	Group 2	No. 1/No. 2	6	6	6	6	6	6	8	8
30.1 (2060)	Group 1	Sel Str	4	4	4	6	6	6	6	6
to	Group 1	No. 1/No. 2	4	4	6	6	6	6	6	6
35 (2400)	Group 2	Sel Str	4	6	6	6	6	6	6	6
	Group 2	No. 1/No. 2	6	6	6	6	6	8	8	8
35.1 (2405)	Group 1	Sel Str	4	4	4	6	6	6	6	6
to	Group 1	No. 1/No. 2	4	6	6	6	6	6	6	8
40 (2740)	Group 2	Sel Str	4	6	6	6	6	6	6	6
	Group 2	No. 1/No. 2	6	6	6	6	6	8	8	8
40.1 (2750)	Group 1	Sel Str	4	4	4	6	6	6	6	6
to	Group 1	No. 1/No. 2	4	6	6	6	6	6	6	8
45 (3085)	Group 2	Sel Str	6	6	6	6	6	6	6	8
	Group 2	No. 1/No. 2	6	6	6	6	6	8	8	8
45.1 (3090)	Group 1	Sel Str	4	4	4	6	6	6	6	6
to	Group 1	No. 1/No. 2	4	6	6	6	6	6	6	8
50 (3425)	Group 2	Sel Str	6	6	6	6	6	6	6	8
	Group 2	No. 1/No. 2	6	6	6	6	6	8	8	8

Notes:
1. 4 is a 38 x 89mm stud (2 x 4 in.)
2. 6 is a 38 x 140mm stud (2 x 6 in.)
3. 8 is a 38 x 184mm stud (2 x 8 in.)
4. 10 is a 38 x 235mm stud (2 x 10 in.)
5. Species Group 1 is S-P-F, D.Fir-L, Hem-Fir
6. Species Group 2 is Northern Species Group
7. Tabulated sizes were calculated using Imperial dimensions for stud length, stud spacing and backfill height.

PWF Stud Selection Tables

Wood Sleeper or Slab on Grade

3.0m 400mm

Stud length = 3.0m (10 ft.)
Stud spacing = 400mm (16 in.)

Vertical load range kN/m (plf)	Species	Grade	Backfill height, m (ft.-in.) 1.2 (4-0)	1.4 (4-6)	1.5 (5-0)	1.7 (5-6)	1.8 (6-0)	2 (6-6)	2.1 (7-0)	2.3 (7-6)
15 (1030)	Group 1	Sel Str	6	6	6	6	8	8	8	10
to	Group 1	No. 1/No. 2	6	6	6	8	8	10	10	10
20 (1370)	Group 2	Sel Str	6	6	6	8	8	10	10	10
	Group 2	No. 1/No. 2	6	8	8	10	10	10	n/a	n/a
20.1 (1375)	Group 1	Sel Str	6	6	6	6	8	8	8	10
to	Group 1	No. 1/No. 2	6	6	8	8	8	10	10	n/a
25 (1715)	Group 2	Sel Str	6	6	8	8	8	10	10	10
	Group 2	No. 1/No. 2	6	8	8	10	10	n/a	n/a	n/a
25.1 (1720)	Group 1	Sel Str	6	6	6	6	8	8	8	10
to	Group 1	No. 1/No. 2	6	6	8	8	10	10	10	n/a
30 (2055)	Group 2	Sel Str	6	6	8	8	8	10	10	n/a
	Group 2	No. 1/No. 2	8	8	8	10	10	n/a	n/a	n/a
30.1 (2060)	Group 1	Sel Str	6	6	6	6	8	8	8	10
to	Group 1	No. 1/No. 2	6	6	8	8	10	10	10	n/a
35 (2400)	Group 2	Sel Str	6	8	8	8	10	10	10	n/a
	Group 2	No. 1/No. 2	8	8	8	10	10	n/a	n/a	n/a
35.1 (2405)	Group 1	Sel Str	6	6	6	8	8	8	8	10
to	Group 1	No. 1/No. 2	6	8	8	8	10	10	10	n/a
40 (2740)	Group 2	Sel Str	6	8	8	8	10	10	10	n/a
	Group 2	No. 1/No. 2	8	8	10	10	10	n/a	n/a	n/a
40.1 (2750)	Group 1	Sel Str	6	6	6	8	8	8	8	10
to	Group 1	No. 1/No. 2	6	8	8	8	10	10	10	n/a
45 (3085)	Group 2	Sel Str	6	8	8	8	10	10	10	n/a
	Group 2	No. 1/No. 2	8	8	10	10	10	n/a	n/a	n/a
45.1 (3090)	Group 1	Sel Str	6	6	6	8	8	8	10	10
to	Group 1	No. 1/No. 2	6	8	8	8	10	10	10	n/a
50 (3425)	Group 2	Sel Str	8	8	8	8	10	10	10	n/a
	Group 2	No. 1/No. 2	8	8	10	10	n/a	n/a	n/a	n/a

Notes:
1. 4 is a 38 x 89mm stud (2 x 4 in.)
2. 6 is a 38 x 140mm stud (2 x 6 in.)
3. 8 is a 38 x 184mm stud (2 x 8 in.)
4. 10 is a 38 x 235mm stud (2 x 10 in.)
5. Species Group 1 is S-P-F, D.Fir-L, Hem-Fir
6. Species Group 2 is Northern Species Group
7. Tabulated sizes were calculated using Imperial dimensions for stud length, stud spacing and backfill height.

PWF Stud Selection Tables

3.0m 300mm

Wood Sleeper or Slab on Grade

Stud length = 3.0m (10 ft.)
Stud spacing = 300mm (12 in.)

Vertical load range kN/m (plf)	Species	Grade	Backfill height, m (ft.-in.) 1.2 (4-0)	1.5 (5-0)	1.8 (6-0)	2.1 (7-0)	2.4 (8-0)	2.6 (8-6)	2.7 (9-0)	2.9 (9-6)
15 (1030)	Group 1	Sel Str	6	6	6	8	8	10	10	10
to	Group 1	No. 1/No. 2	6	6	8	8	10	10	n/a	n/a
20 (1370)	Group 2	Sel Str	6	6	8	8	10	10	n/a	n/a
	Group 2	No. 1/No. 2	6	6	8	10	n/a	n/a	n/a	n/a
20.1 (1375)	Group 1	Sel Str	6	6	6	8	8	10	10	10
to	Group 1	No. 1/No. 2	6	6	8	8	10	10	n/a	n/a
25 (1715)	Group 2	Sel Str	6	6	8	8	10	10	n/a	n/a
	Group 2	No. 1/No. 2	6	8	8	10	n/a	n/a	n/a	n/a
25.1 (1720)	Group 1	Sel Str	6	6	6	8	8	10	10	10
to	Group 1	No. 1/No. 2	6	6	8	10	10	10	n/a	n/a
30 (2055)	Group 2	Sel Str	6	6	8	10	10	10	n/a	n/a
	Group 2	No. 1/No. 2	6	8	10	10	n/a	n/a	n/a	n/a
30.1 (2060)	Group 1	Sel Str	6	6	6	8	8	10	10	10
to	Group 1	No. 1/No. 2	6	6	8	10	10	n/a	n/a	n/a
35 (2400)	Group 2	Sel Str	6	6	8	10	10	10	n/a	n/a
	Group 2	No. 1/No. 2	6	8	10	10	n/a	n/a	n/a	n/a
35.1 (2405)	Group 1	Sel Str	6	6	6	8	8	10	10	10
to	Group 1	No. 1/No. 2	6	6	8	10	10	n/a	n/a	n/a
40 (2740)	Group 2	Sel Str	6	6	8	10	10	n/a	n/a	n/a
	Group 2	No. 1/No. 2	6	8	10	10	n/a	n/a	n/a	n/a
40.1 (2750)	Group 1	Sel Str	6	6	6	8	8	10	10	10
to	Group 1	No. 1/No. 2	6	6	8	10	10	n/a	n/a	n/a
45 (3085)	Group 2	Sel Str	6	6	8	10	10	n/a	n/a	n/a
	Group 2	No. 1/No. 2	6	8	10	10	n/a	n/a	n/a	n/a
45.1 (3090)	Group 1	Sel Str	6	6	6	8	8	10	10	10
to	Group 1	No. 1/No. 2	6	6	8	10	10	n/a	n/a	n/a
50 (3425)	Group 2	Sel Str	6	8	8	10	10	n/a	n/a	n/a
	Group 2	No. 1/No. 2	6	8	10	10	n/a	n/a	n/a	n/a

Notes:
1. 4 is a 38 x 89mm stud (2 x 4 in.)
2. 6 is a 38 x 140mm stud (2 x 6 in.)
3. 8 is a 38 x 184mm stud (2 x 8 in.)
4. 10 is a 38 x 235mm stud (2 x 10 in.)
5. Species Group 1 is S-P-F, D.Fir-L, Hem-Fir
6. Species Group 2 is Northern Species Group
7. Tabulated sizes were calculated using Imperial dimensions for stud length, stud spacing and backfill height.

PWF Stud Selection Tables

Wood Sleeper or Slab on Grade

3.0m 200mm

Stud length = 3.0m (10 ft.)
Stud spacing = 200mm (8 in.)

Vertical load range kN/m (plf)	Species	Grade	Backfill height, m (ft.-in.) 1.2 (4-0)	1.5 (5-0)	1.8 (6-0)	2.1 (7-0)	2.4 (8-0)	2.6 (8-6)	2.7 (9-0)	2.9 (9-6)
15 (1030)	Group 1	Sel Str	4	6	6	6	8	8	8	8
to	Group 1	No. 1/No. 2	4	6	6	6	8	8	10	10
20 (1370)	Group 2	Sel Str	4	6	6	8	8	8	10	10
	Group 2	No. 1/No. 2	6	6	6	8	10	10	10	n/a
20.1 (1375)	Group 1	Sel Str	4	6	6	6	8	8	8	8
to	Group 1	No. 1/No. 2	4	6	6	8	8	8	10	10
25 (1715)	Group 2	Sel Str	4	6	6	8	8	8	10	10
	Group 2	No. 1/No. 2	6	6	6	8	10	10	10	n/a
25.1 (1720)	Group 1	Sel Str	4	6	6	6	8	8	8	8
to	Group 1	No. 1/No. 2	4	6	6	8	8	8	10	10
30 (2055)	Group 2	Sel Str	6	6	6	8	8	8	10	10
	Group 2	No. 1/No. 2	6	6	8	8	10	10	10	n/a
30.1 (2060)	Group 1	Sel Str	4	6	6	6	8	8	8	8
to	Group 1	No. 1/No. 2	6	6	6	8	8	10	10	10
35 (2400)	Group 2	Sel Str	6	6	6	8	8	8	10	10
	Group 2	No. 1/No. 2	6	6	8	8	10	10	10	n/a
35.1 (2405)	Group 1	Sel Str	4	6	6	6	8	8	8	8
to	Group 1	No. 1/No. 2	6	6	6	8	8	10	10	10
40 (2740)	Group 2	Sel Str	6	6	6	8	8	10	10	10
	Group 2	No. 1/No. 2	6	6	8	8	10	10	n/a	n/a
40.1 (2750)	Group 1	Sel Str	6	6	6	6	8	8	8	8
to	Group 1	No. 1/No. 2	6	6	6	8	8	10	10	10
45 (3085)	Group 2	Sel Str	6	6	6	8	8	10	10	10
	Group 2	No. 1/No. 2	6	6	8	8	10	10	n/a	n/a
45.1 (3090)	Group 1	Sel Str	6	6	6	6	8	8	8	8
to	Group 1	No. 1/No. 2	6	6	6	8	8	10	10	10
50 (3425)	Group 2	Sel Str	6	6	6	8	8	10	10	10
	Group 2	No. 1/No. 2	6	6	8	8	10	10	n/a	n/a

Notes:
1. 4 is a 38 x 89mm stud (2 x 4 in.)
2. 6 is a 38 x 140mm stud (2 x 6 in.)
3. 8 is a 38 x 184mm stud (2 x 8 in.)
4. 10 is a 38 x 235mm stud (2 x 10 in.)
5. Species Group 1 is S-P-F, D.Fir-L, Hem-Fir
6. Species Group 2 is Northern Species Group
7. Tabulated sizes were calculated using Imperial dimensions for stud length, stud spacing and backfill height.

Floors

Floors at the top and bottom of permanent wood foundations provide structural rigidity.

7.0 Floors

PWFs have three floor options: a wood sleeper floor, a concrete slab floor or a suspended wood floor. Basement floors and ground floors (floors at the top of foundation) should be installed before backfilling to provide lateral support to resist backfill loads. If either floor is not installed before backfilling, temporary bracing must be adequate to prevent deflection of the walls from the soil backfill.

Wood Sleeper Floor

Wood sleeper floors (Figure 7.1) are strong, warm and economical to construct because they can be built entirely with 38 x 89mm (2 x 4 in.) treated lumber. Intermediate 38 x 89mm (2 x 4 in.) treated wood sleepers are placed flat on the levelled drainage layer at spacings determined by the floor joist spans which, in turn, depend on joist size, species, grade and spacing.

A 0.15mm (6 mil) polyethylene sheet is spread over the granular drainage layer as a dampproofing membrane and for soil gas protection, just as it is under a concrete slab floor. The polyethylene should be no more than 1.2m (4 ft.) wide and overlapped by 300mm (12 in.). The polyethylene sheet should be sealed to the foundation wall footing around its entire perimeter. Depositing a thin layer of sand over the polyethylene will help to keep it in place during construction.

Floor joist spans are found in either the *National Building Code*, provincial codes or in the *Span Book* published by the Canadian Wood Council. For example, treated 38 x 89mm (2 x 4 in.) joists, the most economical size for wood floors, can span about 1.2m (4 ft.) and so would rest on sleepers placed four feet apart.

The floor joists span between wall footings and sleepers. It is good practice to provide end bearing support for each joist. To achieve this bearing at the sidewall may require use of a wider footing than normal or an additional sleeper installed next to the footing. Alternatively, joists can be securely nailed to a rim joist (Figure 7.1).

Joists are either toe-nailed into a rim joist which is nailed to the PWF wall or placed directly in line with the wall studs. Joists should be full length to the centre wall, or, if no centre wall is used, butted and joined with a treated splice plate over the sleeper support. Toe-nail joists to sleepers with two 76mm (3 in.) nails. Floor stiffness can be increased by blocking between joists, above each row of sleepers.

At end walls, where floor joists run parallel to the wall, increased nailing and blocking are needed to transfer lateral soil loads to the sleeper floor to prevent inward movement of the wall. The amount of increased lateral support depends on backfill heights. See Figure 7.1, Detail B.

Normally the first joist parallel to the end wall is nailed to the end wall studs but, with backfill heights greater than 1.5m (5 ft.), a second joist should be nailed to the first joist.

All penetrations of the floor by pipes, floor drains or other objects must be sealed with, for example, acoustic caulking to the polyethylene ground cover, to prevent water vapour and soil gas leakage.

Figure 7.1
Wood sleeper floor

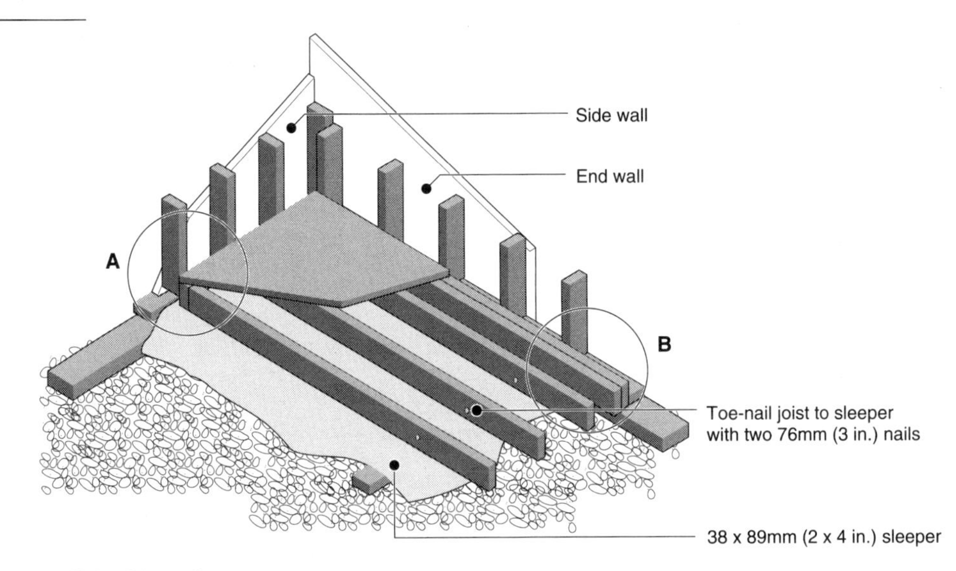

Detail A: side wall

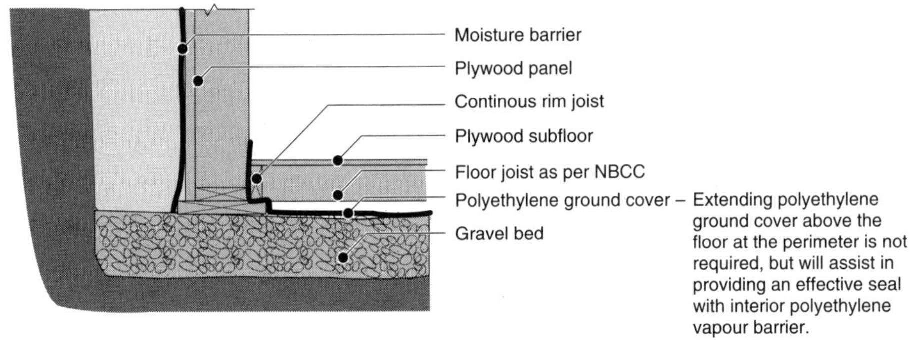

Detail B: end wall

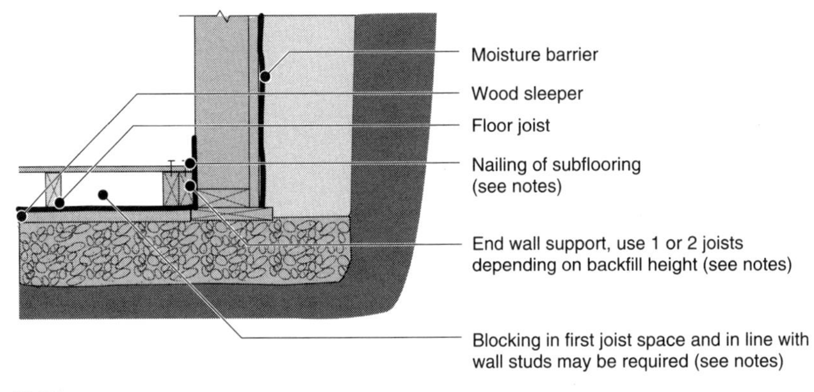

Notes:

1. **When backfill height is 1.5m (5 ft.) or less:** Use one 38 x 89mm (2 x 4 in.) joist at end wall. Nail subflooring with one row 51mm (2 in.) nails at 150mm (6 in.) o.c. No blocking required in first joist space.
2. **When backfill height is greater than 1.5m (5 ft.):** Use two 38 x 89mm (2 x 4 in.) joist at end wall. Nail subflooring with two rows 51mm (2 in.) nails at 75mm (3 in.) o.c. 38 x 89mm (2 x 4 in.) blocking required in first joist space and in line with wall studs.

Concrete Slab Floor

Concrete slab floors should be at least 75mm (3 in.) thick exclusive of concrete topping and placed in accordance with NBCC requirements. The concrete is poured over the polyethylene sheet which covers the granular drainage layer. As with the wood sleeper floor, the polyethylene should be lapped and sealed to the foundation footing around its entire perimeter.

The concrete slab butts directly against the inside edge of the wall studs to resist horizontal loads on the foundation. Bearing height between the slab and and studs should be at least 25mm (1 in.) (Figure 7.2). The slab may be poured right into the stud space, or, preferably, it can bear against a continuous wood strip along the inside lower edge of the foundation wall. The strip serves as a screed board for levelling the slab. All penetrations of the floor slab by pipes, floor drains or other objects should be sealed against water vapour or soil gas leakage.

Figure 7.2
Concrete slab floor

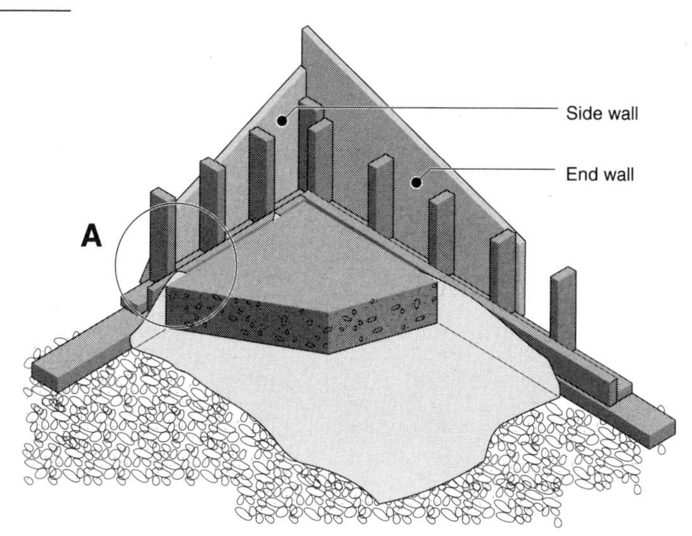

Detail A

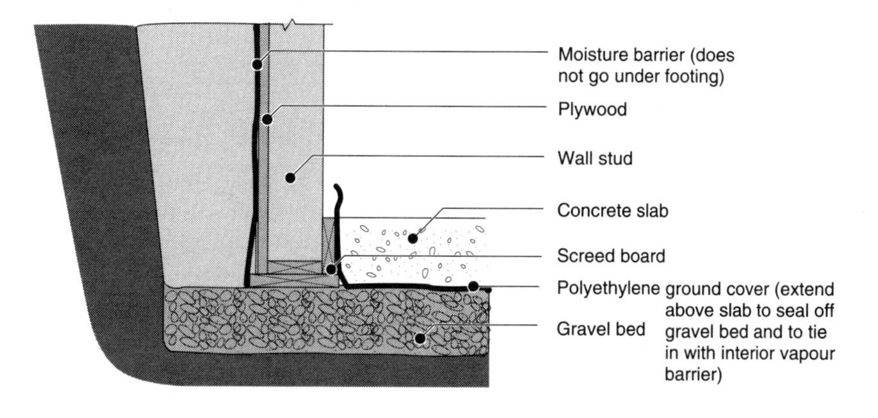

Suspended Wood Floor

Suspended wood floors allow the foundation to resist higher than normal backfill by using longer studs and providing an intermediate wall support, in the form of the raised basement floor, above the footing. Joist sizes and spacings for suspended wood floors follow the NBCC requirements for conventional floor framing.

The greater wall height with this type of PWF creates a horizontal joint in the plywood sheathing at the level of the suspended floor. Blocking used to back this joint also acts as a nailer for the bottom edge of interior finishes and provides firestopping required by NBCC (Figure 7.3).

At side walls, joists should be in line with the foundation wall studs and supported on a 38 x 140mm (2 x 6 in.) ledger nailed to the studs. Joists should be butted together in line over the interior support bearing wall and nailed directly to the bearing wall (Figure 7.3, Detail B).

As with sleeper floors, extra support is required at end walls where the joists run parallel to the wall. With backfill heights of 2m (6-1/2 ft.) or less, the first joist parallel to the end wall is doubled by nailing a second 38 x 89mm (2 x 4 in.) joist to the first joist. The doubled joist offers greater surface area for increased nailing of the subfloor, thereby improving the lateral load capacity of the floor (Figure 7.3, Detail C).

Where end wall backfill heights exceed 2m (6-1/2 ft.), requirements for strengthening the floor include installing 38 x 89mm (2 x 4 in.) blocking between the first two rows of floor joists and reinforcing the second joist by nailing a 38 x 89mm (2 x 4 in.) joist to it. The blocking and additional joists can be prefabricated in the shape of a ladder and then fitted between the appropriate floor joists.

The polyethylene sheet is installed over the granular layer as for the sleeper floor.

Plywood subflooring installed over the floor joists acts as a diaphragm to resist lateral earth loads. Plywood thickness conforms to NBCC requirements for subfloors.

Outside plumbing lines can pass through the foundation wall at the level of, or just below, the floor joists depending on the depth of frost penetration. After the plumbing is installed the openings should be well sealed against moisture and soil gas penetration. This eliminates burying the lines below the footings, and allows access to service lines for drain cleanouts and pipe connections.

Figure 7.3a
Suspended wood floor

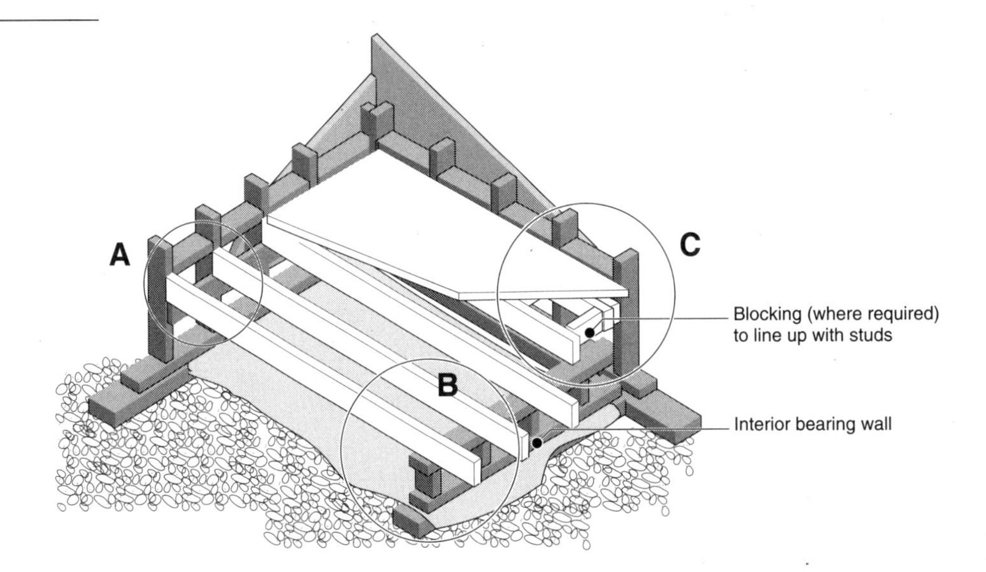

Figure 7.3b
Suspended wood floor and interior bearing wall

Detail A

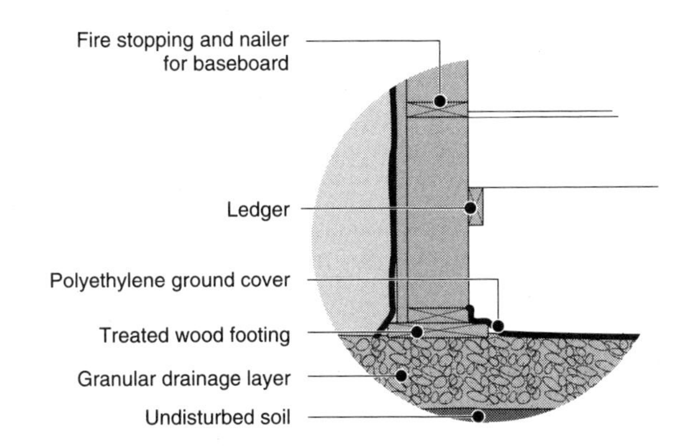

Detail B

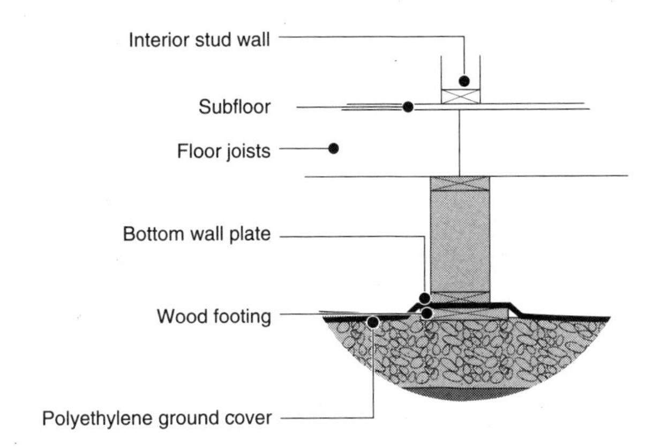

Figure 7.3c
Suspended wood floor nailing and blocking details

Detail C: end wall nailing for suspended wood floor, backfill height 2m (6 ft.-6 in.) or less

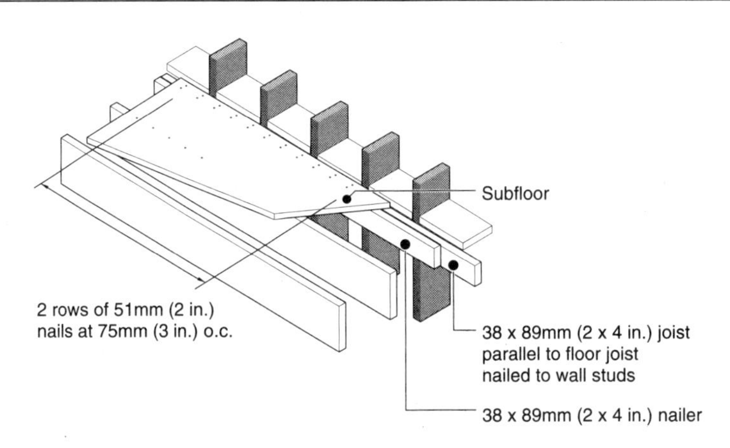

Detail C: end wall nailing for suspended wood floor, backfill height greater than 2m (6 ft.-6 in.)

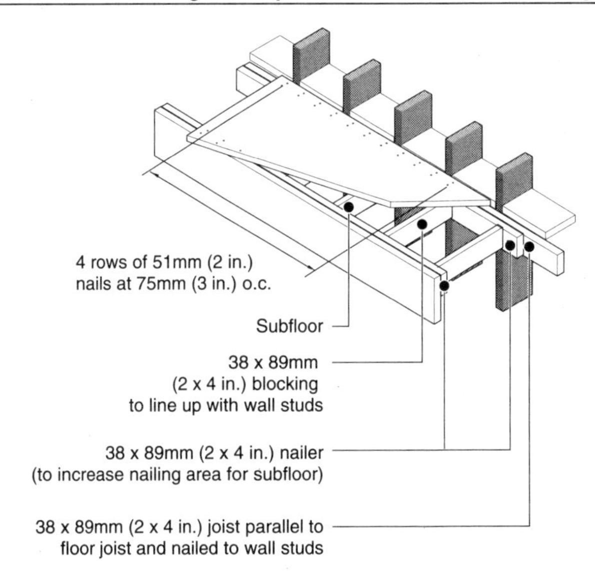

Floors at the Top of Foundation

Special requirements are needed to transfer lateral loads at the top of the foundation wall into the ground floor to prevent inward movement of the wall. Parallel chord wood floor trusses or I-joists may be used instead of solid sawn joists to provide longer spans that can reduce the number of support columns or load-bearing walls required. They must be installed with adequate lateral bracing and blocking to prevent twisting or overturning.

Figure 7.4 illustrates methods to support floor joists resting on bearing walls.

Figure 7.4
Floor joist support on interior bearing walls

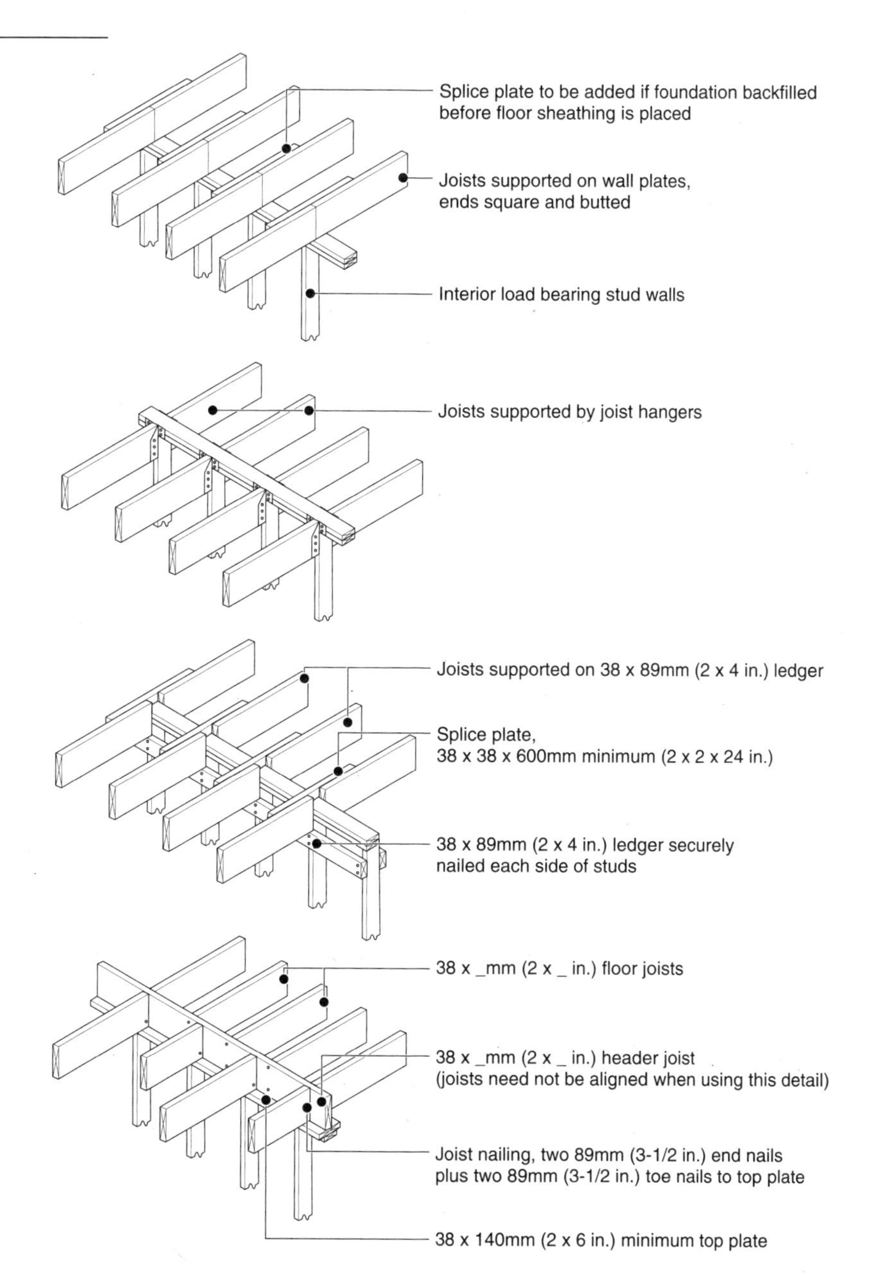

Support for Side Walls

Lumber Joists

At side walls, the joists either frame into the wall studs using joist hangers (Figure 7.5) or rest on the top plate directly over the PWF wall studs. In the latter case the joists are nailed to both header and top plate. When backfill heights are greater than 1.5m (5 ft.) with wood sleeper or concrete slab floors, or greater than 2m (6 ft.) with suspended wood floors, framing straps must be nailed to the top of every stud to better secure the ground floor to the foundation (Figure 7.5, Detail A).

Top-Chord Bearing Trusses

Wood floor trusses that bear on the PWF wall from their top chords must be designed as "top-chord bearing" trusses. They are attached to the tops of PWF walls using framing straps nailed to the ends of the top chord and the inner face of the wall studs (Figure 7.5, Detail C).

Bottom-Chord Bearing Trusses and I-joists

Bottom-chord bearing trusses or wood I-joists are attached using:

- steel hangers or a wood ledger that provide positive bearing of the chord end against the top of the PWF wall studs (Figure 7.5, Detail D), or
- other engineered methods that transfer lateral soil loads from the PWF wall studs to the ground floor.

With bottom chord bearing applications, it is important to ensure that fastening and bracing is adequate to prevent twisting and overturning of trusses or I-joists.

Design

In either case, the trusses and I-joists must be designed to resist the lateral soil load pressures as well as vertical loads.

Figure 7.5
Framing at side wall at top of foundation

Detail A: side wall with floor joist

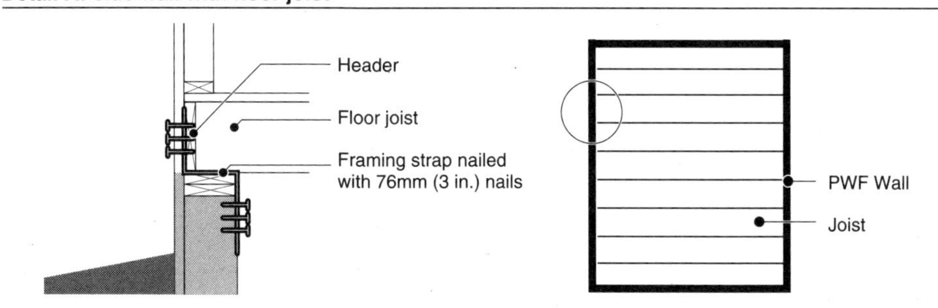

Detail B: side wall with floor joist – alternate

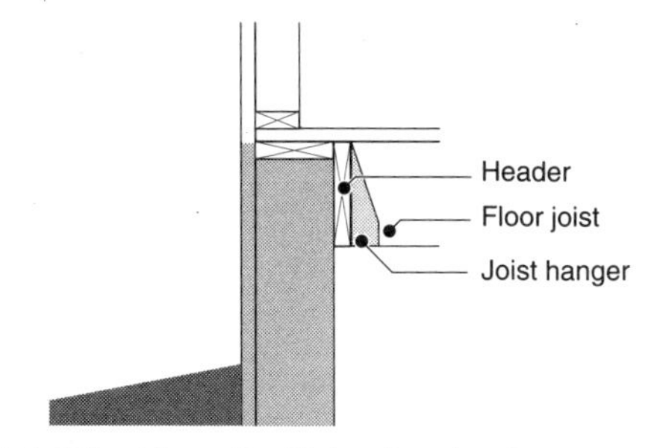

Detail C: side wall with top bearing truss

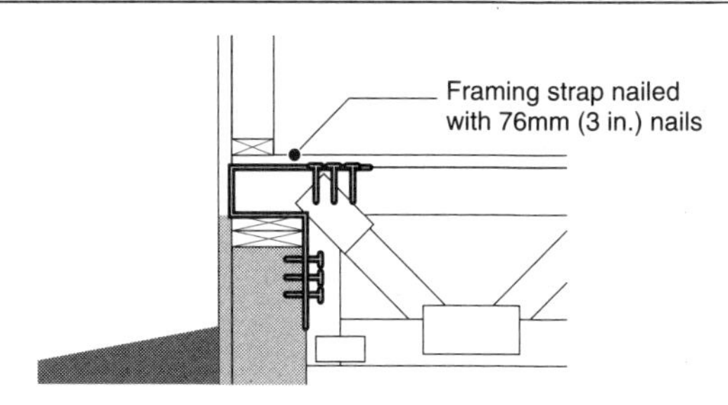

Detail D: side wall with truss or I-joist – alternate

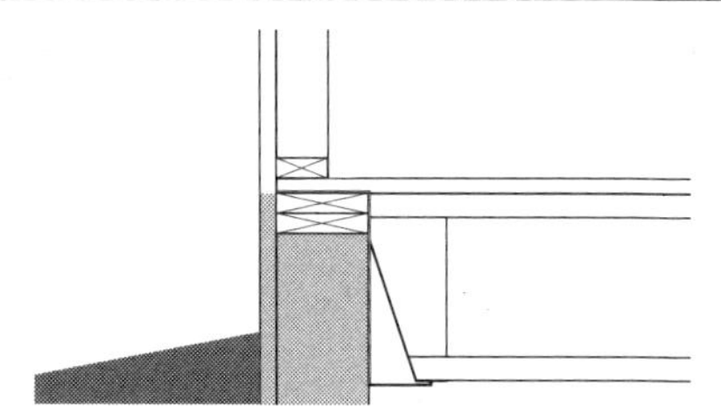

Notes:

1. Where floor joists sit on top wall plates (Detail A), framing straps are required at every stud if backfill height is greater than 1.5m (5 ft.) for concrete slab floor or wood sleeper floor and greater than 2.0m (6.5 ft.) for suspended floor.
2. Where joists frame directly into stud wall (Detail B), framing straps are not required.

Support for End Walls

Lumber Joists

At end walls, where joists run parallel to the wall, full depth blocking, increased nailing and additional framing members are needed between the first two floor joists to transfer lateral loads from the end wall studs into the subfloor.

Where backfill height is more than 1.5m (5 ft.) with a wood sleeper or concrete slab floor, or more than 2m (6-1/2 ft.) with a suspended wood floor, the first joist from the end wall must be reinforced with a 38 x 89mm (2 x 4 in.) joist. Blocking is installed in line with the studs. See Figures 7.6 and 7.7 for nailing requirements and framing details.

Trusses and Wood I-joists

Where the top chords of floor trusses or I-joists are located at the same level as the foundation top plates, blocking is installed in line between the stud and the first floor truss from the end wall (Figure 7.7, Detail C). Increased nailing of the subfloor to the top chord of the truss (see Table 6.1) will help to transfer loads to the floor.

This method of providing load transfer through the top chords of trusses and I-joists is preferred over load transfer in the bottom chords. The method gives better load transfer into the subfloor and minimizes the possibility of twisting trusses and I-joists in reaction to high backfill loads.

Bottom Chord Bearing Trusses and I-joists

Where I-joists or floor trusses rest on top of the foundation wall, inward movement of the foundation wall is sometimes prevented by:

- blocking or diagonal bracing installed so that lateral loads are transferred upward into the floor at a distance from the wall at least two times the depth of the truss or I-joist, or
- with equal backfill on opposite walls, by blocking installed in a continuous line between opposite end walls.

It is very important that blocking and fastening be sufficient to transfer lateral loads from the walls to the blocking or bracing. Adequate blocking and nailing to transfer loads to the subfloor is especially critical when using deep trusses and I-joists.

Figure 7.6
Framing at end wall at top of foundation

Concrete slab or sleeper floor – backfill height 1.5m (5 ft.) or less; or Suspended wood floor – backfill height 2.0m (6.5 ft.) or less

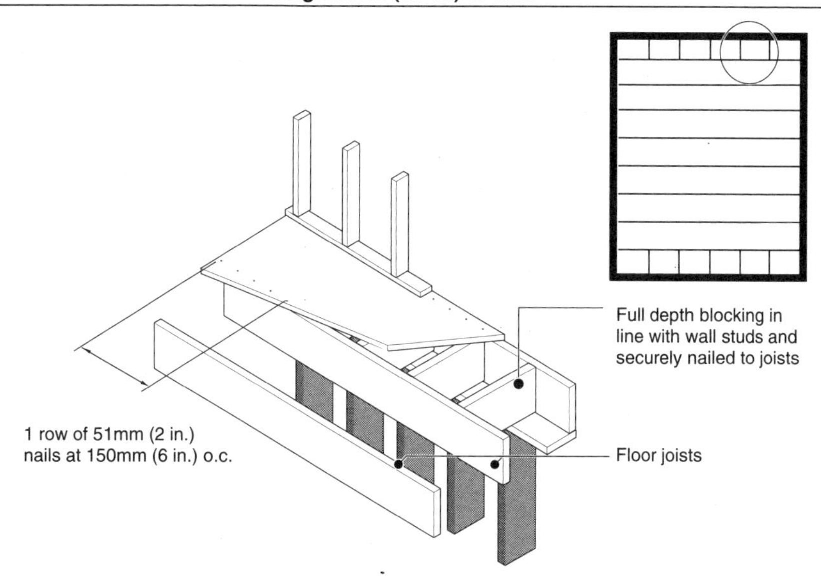

Concrete slab or sleeper floor – backfill height greater than 1.5m (5 ft.); or Suspended wood floor – backfill height greater than 2.0m (6.5 ft.)

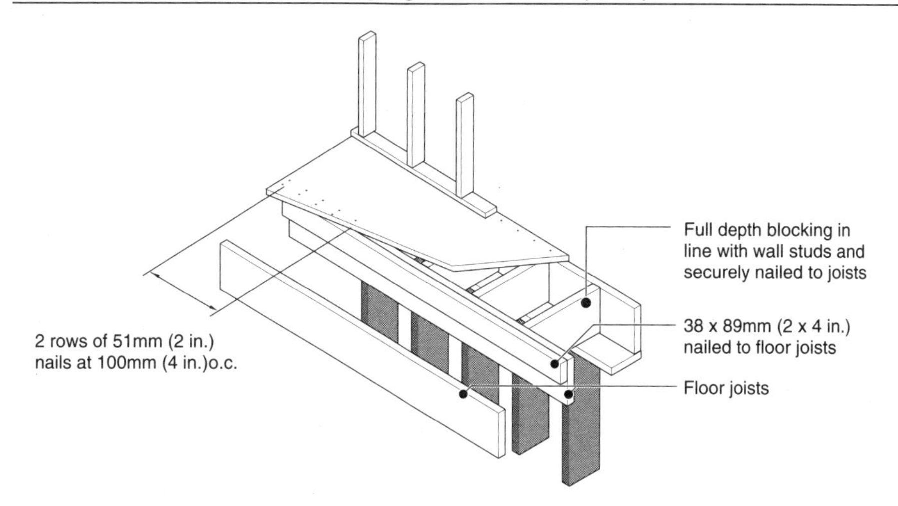

Figure 7.7
End wall connections at top of foundation

Detail A: end wall

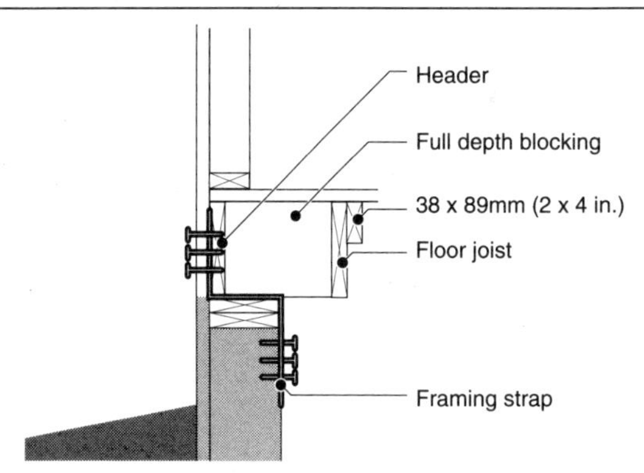

Detail B: end wall – alternate

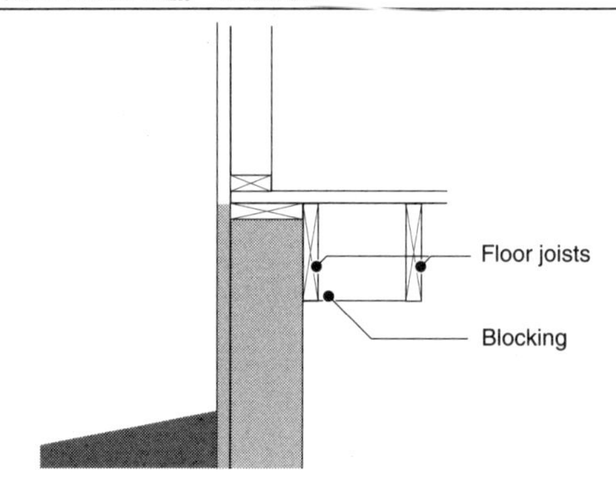

Detail C: end wall with truss or I-joist

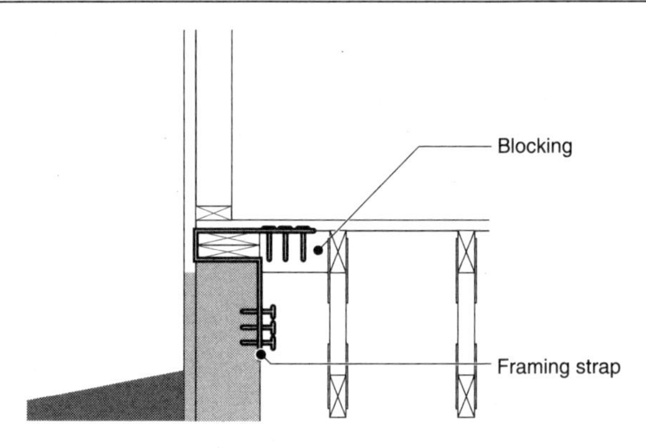

Notes:
1. Framing straps are required at every stud if backfill height is greater than 1.5m (5 ft.) for wood sleeper or concrete slab floor and is greater than 2.0m (6.5 ft.) for suspended floor.

Beam Pocket at End Wall

Main floor support beams should be constructed to the requirements of the *National Building Code.* The beam ends are supported in beam pockets, constructed with pressure treated lumber as shown in Figure 7.8. For beams supporting two storeys above the foundation, the beam support members should be built-up from 38 x _mm (2 x _ in.) lumber or greater unless engineering calculations show that smaller members can be used.

Figure 7.8a
Methods of framing beam pocket and supporting framing at end wall

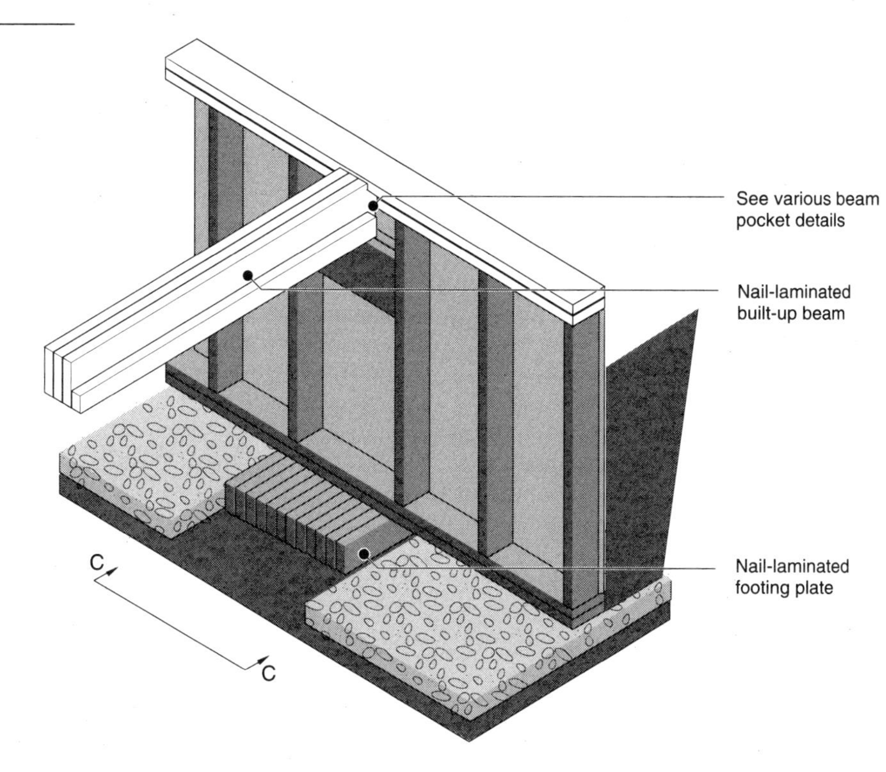

Section CC: footing

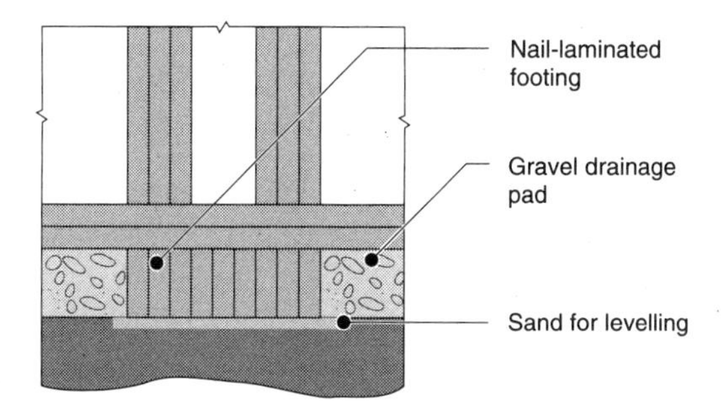

Figure 7.8b
Methods of framing beam pocket and supporting framing at end wall – floor at top of PWF wall

End view

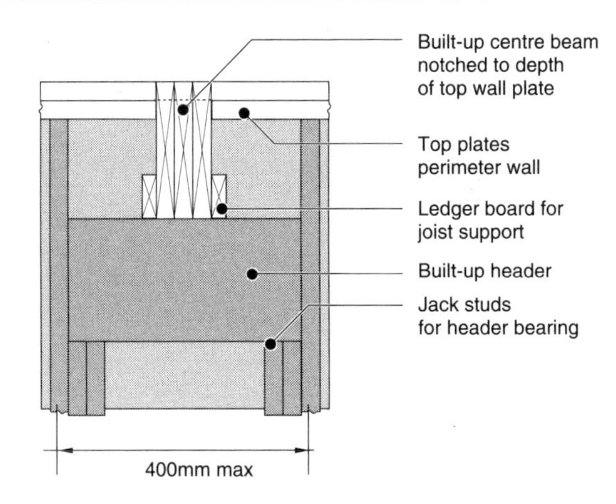

Elevation

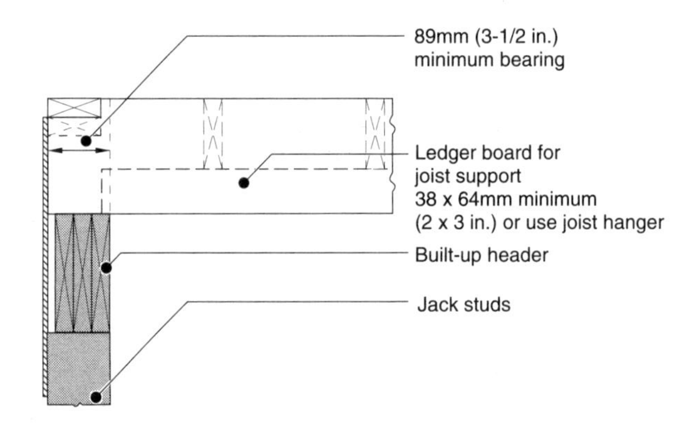

Figure 7.8c
Methods of framing beam pocket and supporting framing at end wall – floor at top of PWF wall, alternate detail

End view

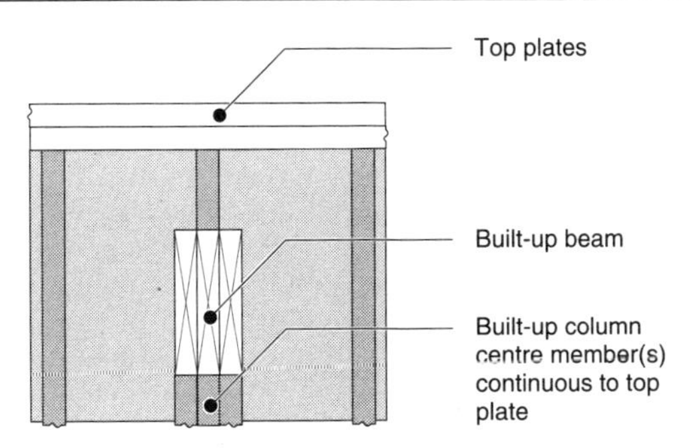

Elevation

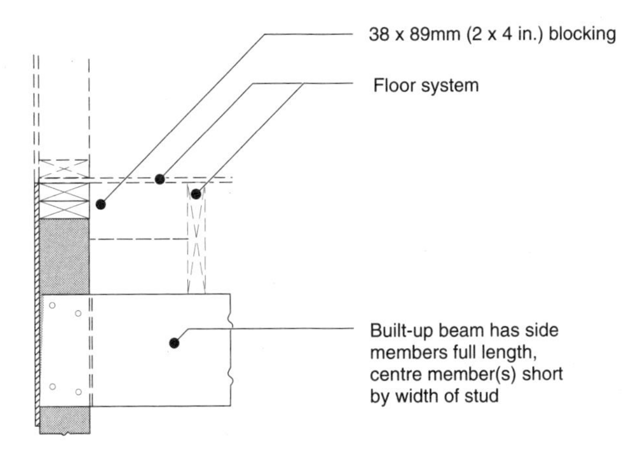

Plan view

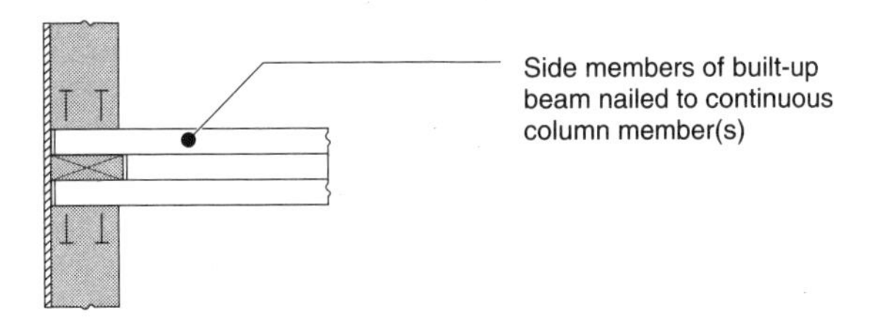

Figure 7.8d
Methods of framing beam pocket and supporting framing at end wall – floor at top of PWF wall, alternate detail

End view

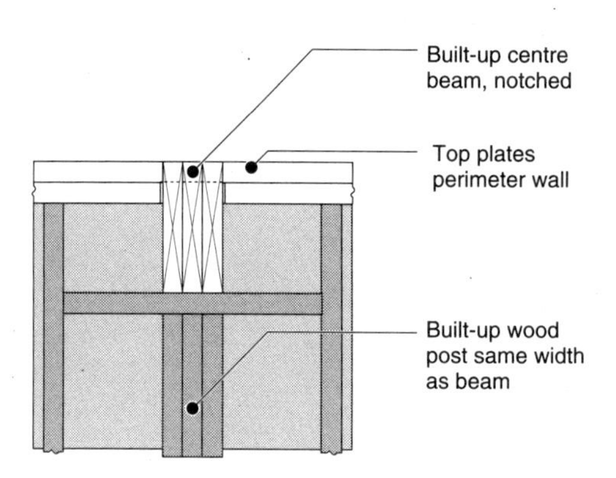

Elevation

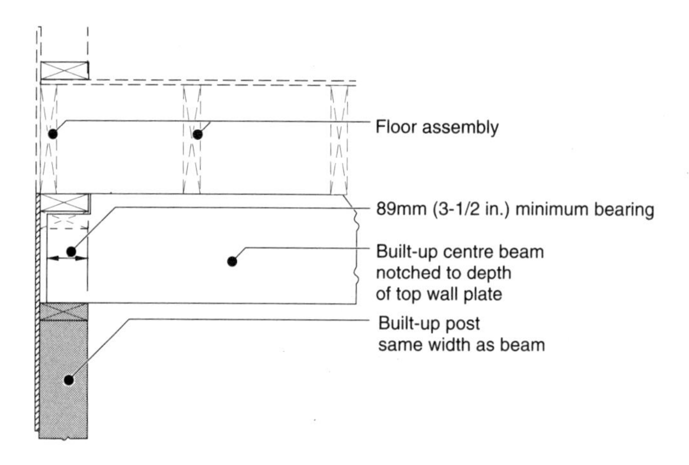

Figure 7.8e
Methods of framing beam pocket and supporting framing at end wall – floor at top of PWF wall, alternate detail

End view

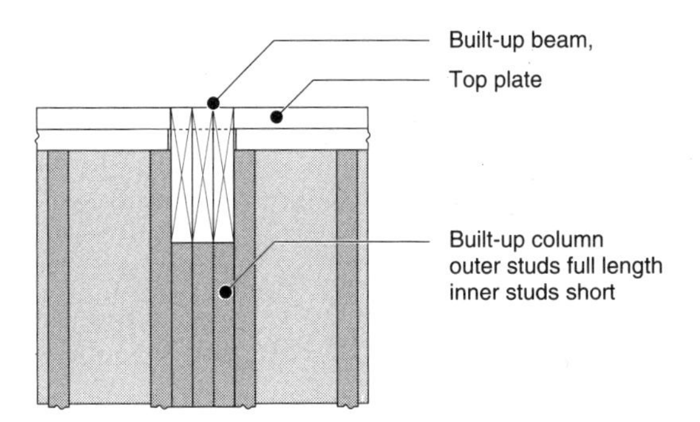

Elevation

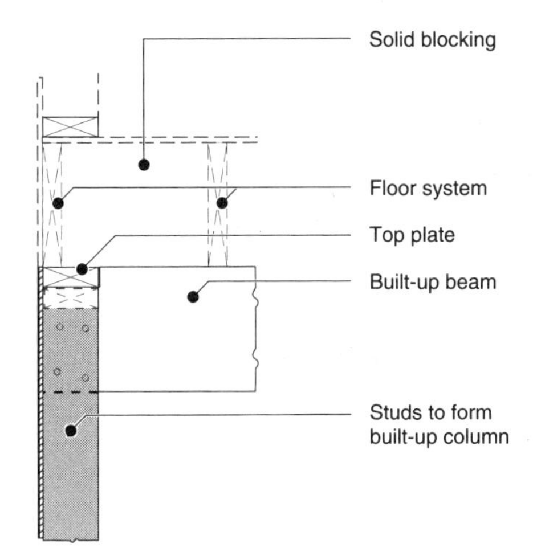

Stairwell Framing

Stairwells located more than 1.2m (4 ft.) from the side wall or more than 1.8m (6 ft.) from the end wall can be framed using standard methods. Stairwells located closer to side walls and end walls or at corners require increased nailing and special framing to provide lateral resistance against soil loads at the top of the foundation.

Framing at Side Wall

Stairwell openings less than 1.2m (4 ft.) from the foundation side wall must be framed with a multi-ply stairwell beam as shown in Figure 7.9. The joists on either side of the opening are strengthened by trimmer joists.

Figure 7.9
Stairwell framing within 1.2m (4 ft.) of side wall

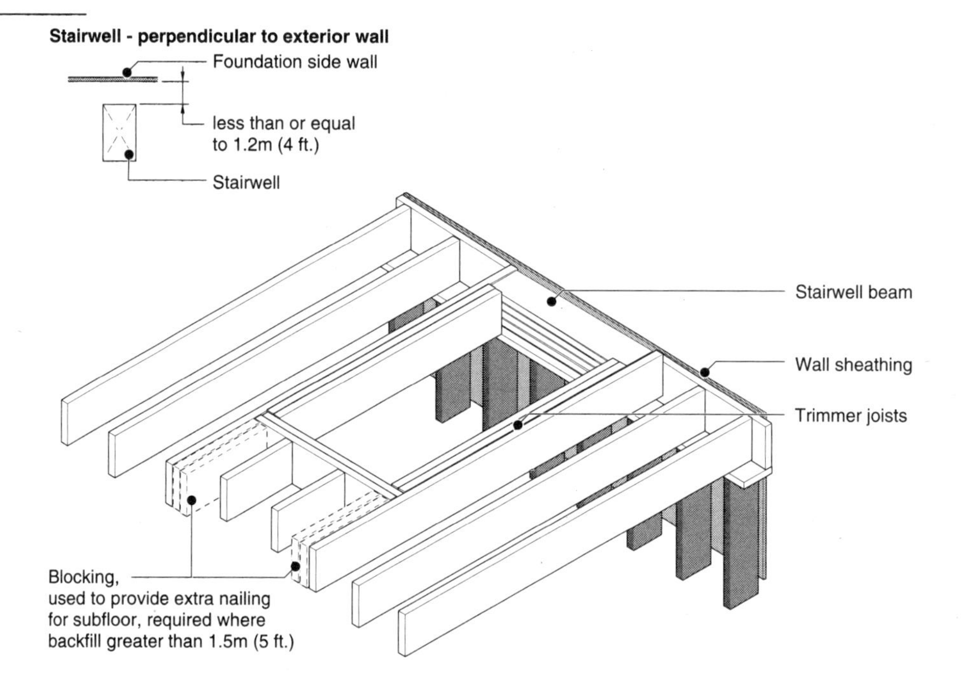

Framing at End Wall

Openings less than 1.8m (6 ft.) from the end wall also require a multi-ply stairwell beam, along with doubled headers and trimmer joists. See Figure 7.10.

Figure 7.10
Stairwell framing within 1.8m (6 ft.) of end wall

Stairwell - parallel to exterior wall

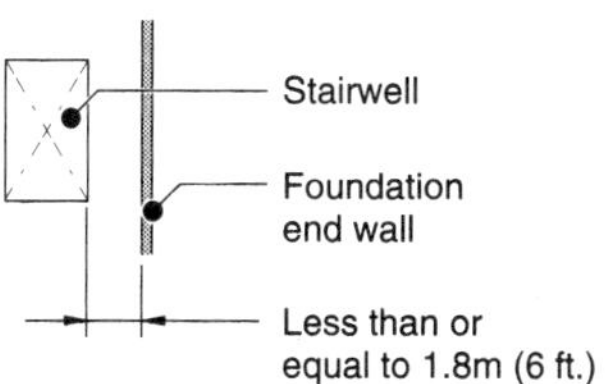

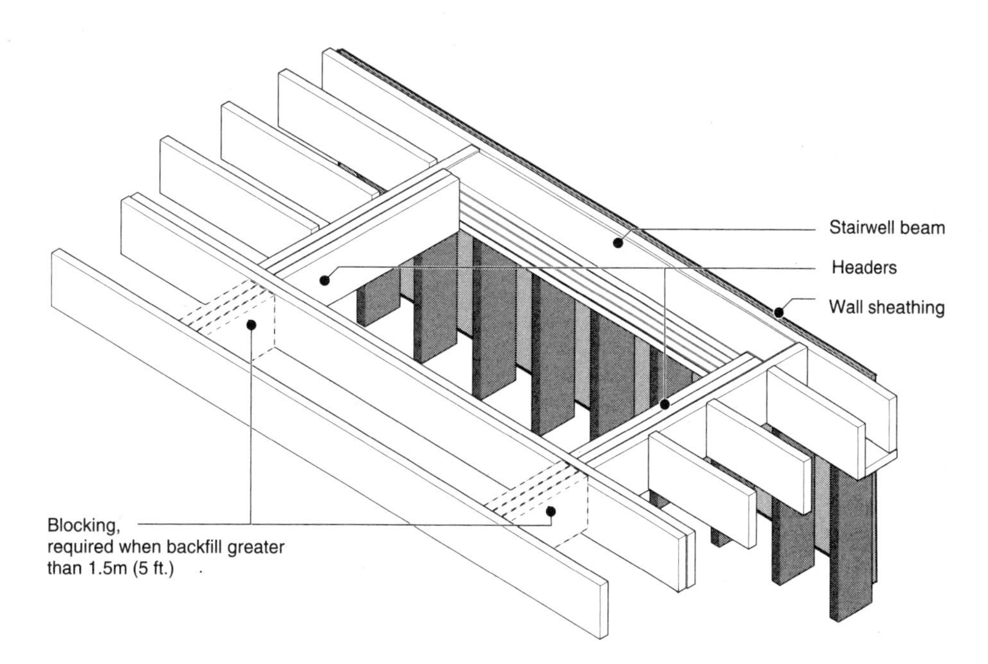

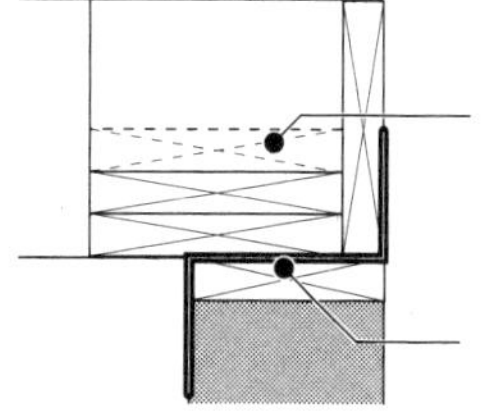

Framing at Corners and at Split Level Entrances

Stairwells located at corners must be carefully framed to resist lateral loads from the soil backfill. As shown in Figure 7.11, this requires lapped stairwell beams, blocking and multi-member headers.

At split level entrances, floor joists for the landing butt directly against the foundation wall studs and the whole landing is firmly anchored to resist lateral thrust from the foundation wall See Figure 7.5.

Figure 7.11
Framing of a corner stairwell

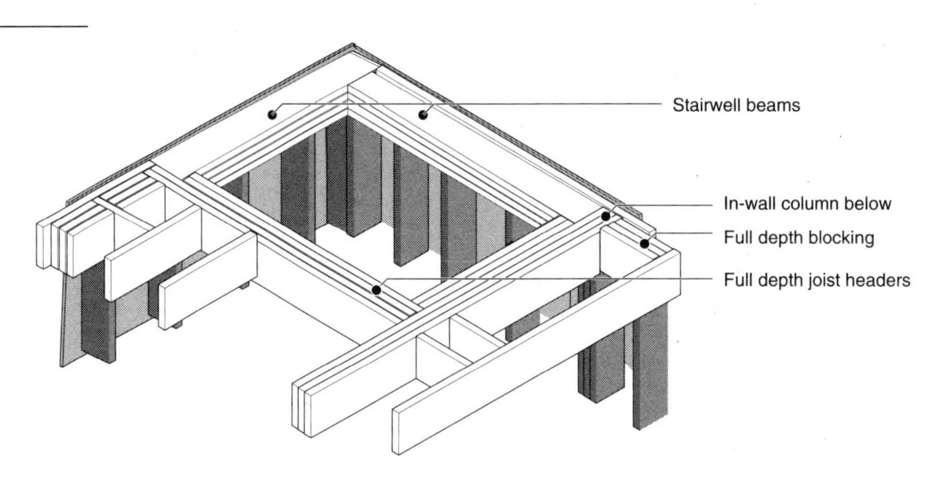

Section of corner detail

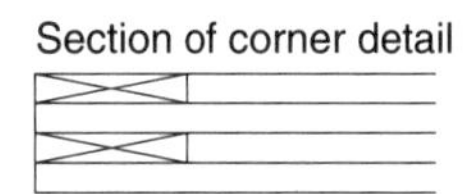

Table 7.1
Framing and nailing of stairwell openings (For use with Figures 7.9 to 7.11)

	Stairwell opening width, m (ft.-in.)	Backfill height, m (ft.-in.)	Number of stairwell beam laminations 38 x 140 (2 x 6)	38 x 184 (2 x 8)	38 x 235 (2 x 10)	Min. no. of joist headers	Nailing of subfloor to framing around opening, 76mm (3 in.) nails
wood sleeper or concrete slab floors	up to 3.2 (10-6)	1.5 (6)	3	2	–	2	2 rows, 6 in.o.c.
		2.3 (7-6)	9	6	4	3	2 rows, 2 in o.c.
		2.9 (9-6)	–	10	7	3	2 rows, 2 in o.c.
	not greater than 3.6 (12)	1.5 (6)	3	3	2	2	2 rows, 6 in o.c.
		2.3 (7-6)	11	8	5	3	2 rows, 2 in o.c.
		2.9 (9-6)	–	12	8	3	2 rows, 2 in o.c.
	not greater than 4.3 (14)	1.5 (6)	5	3	2	2	2 rows, 6 in o.c.
		2.3 (7-6)	–	11	8	3	2 rows, 2 in o.c.
		2.9 (9-6)	–	–	12	3	2 rows, 2 in o.c.
suspended wood floors	up to 3.2 (10-6)	2 (6-6)	2	–	–	2	2 rows, 6 in o.c.
		2.3 (7-6)	4	3	–	2	2 rows, 2 in o.c.
		2.9 (9-6)	7	5	4	3	2 rows, 2 in o.c.
		3.5 (11-6)	12	8	6	3	2 rows, 2 in o.c.
	not greater than 3.6 (12)	2 (6-6)	2	–	–	2	2 rows, 6 in o.c.
		2.3 (7-6)	4	3	–	2	2 rows, 2 in o.c.
		2.9 (9-6)	9	6	4	3	2 rows, 2 in o.c.
		3.5 (11-6)	–	10	7	3	2 rows, 2 in o.c.
	not greater than 4.3 (14)	2 (6-6)	3	2	–	2	2 rows, 6 in o.c.
		2.3 (7-6)	6	4	3	2	2 rows, 2 in o.c.
		2.9 (9-6)	–	9	6	3	2 rows, 2 in o.c.
		3.5 (11-6)	–	–	10	3	2 rows, 2 in o.c.

Notes:
1. Individual members in beam laminations should be nailed together with a double row of nails not less than 89mm (3-1/2 in.) in length, spaced not more than 450mm (18 in.) apart in each row with end nails located 100 to 150mm (4 to 6 in.) from the end of each piece.

Moisture Barriers and Backfilling

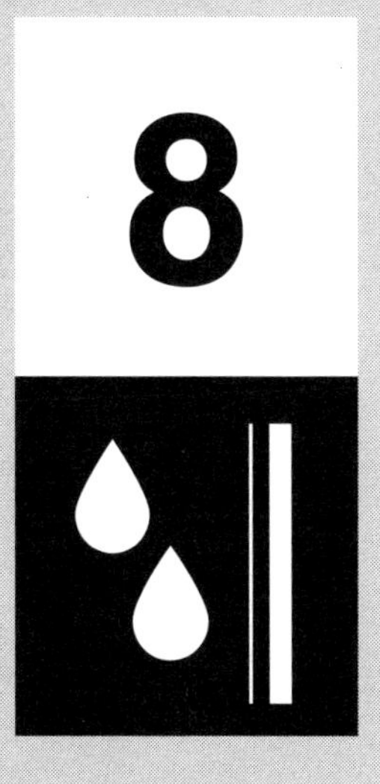

Free-draining backfill should be placed uniformly around the PWF.

8.0 Moisture Barriers and Backfilling

Moisture Barrier Installation

Except for knee walls and crawl spaces with trenched footings (see Chapter 10), the PWF must be protected by a moisture barrier which extends from the grade level down to the footing. The PWF construction standard, CAN/CSA-S406, calls for 0.15mm (6 mil) polyethylene, although as mentioned in Chapter 4, other films or coatings that provide good performance may be used. The barrier is usually installed just before backfilling is to commence.

All joints in the plywood sheathing should have been caulked during construction. Any sharp plywood edges protruding at corners should be smoothed and dirt and

Figure 8.1
Moisture barrier, cover plate and backfill installation

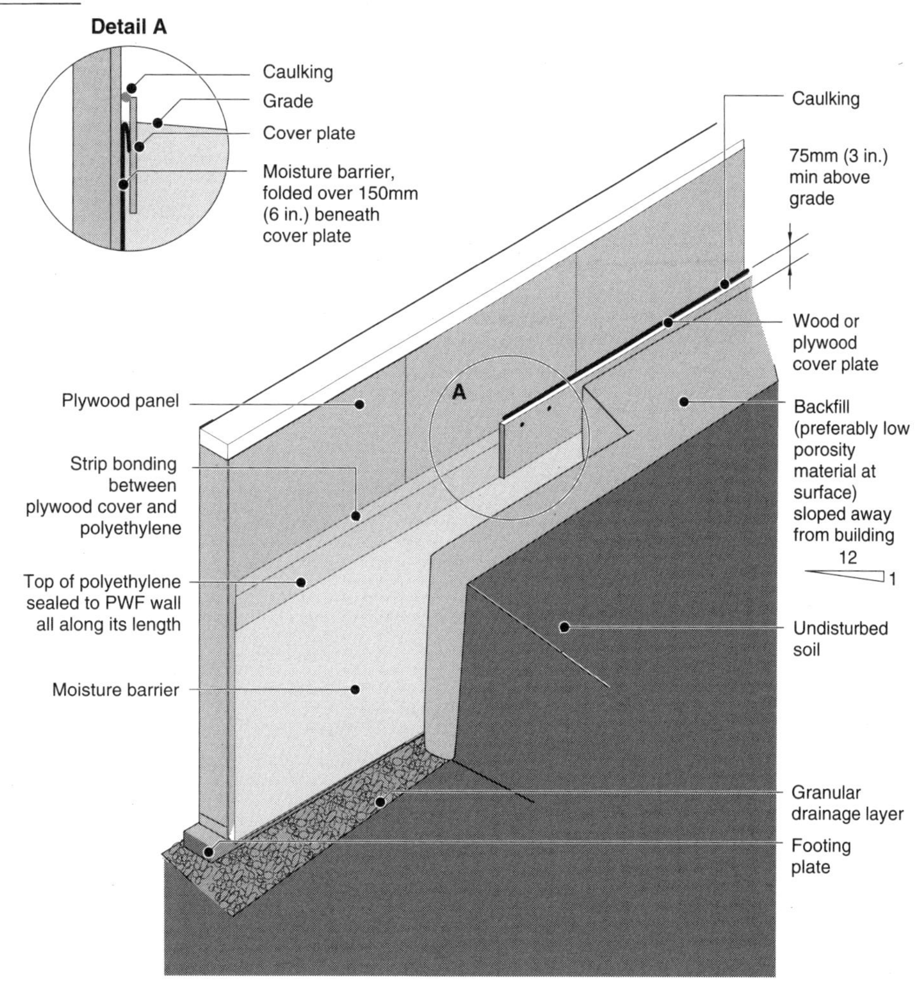

Notes:
1. Caulking shall be compatible with the preservative treated lumber, sheathing and polyethylene moisture barrier.
2. Moisture barrier shall not extend under the footing plate or between the granular drainage layer and the backfill at exterior wall.
3. Strip bonding means application of a suitable caulking in a strip or strips to secure the upper edge of the moisture barrier.

debris cleaned off the exposed part of the footing. The polyethylene should extend down to the footing but not over the granular layer, and not under the wood footing or over the drainage passages of concrete footings where they rest on undisturbed soil as this would inhibit drainage. The top edge of the polyethylene sheet is sealed to the plywood wall all along its length and it is embedded in randomly placed beads of caulking that run vertically up the plywood.

Vertical joints between the polyethylene sheet must be lapped a minimum of 600mm (24 in.) and sealed with caulking. Ensure that adequate polyethylene sheeting is provided at inside corners to prevent ripping caused by the weight of soil during backfilling.

The bottom edge of the polyethylene is not sealed, so that any moisture that becomes trapped behind the barrier can escape. The top edge of the polyethylene must be looped a minimum of 150mm (6 in.) to provide an even edge (Figure 8.1, Detail A), and to provide a double thickness for nailing.

Protection by Coverplate

The top edge of the polyethylene is protected with a treated plywood cover strip at least 12.5mm (1/2 in.) thick and 300mm (12 in.) wide. The top edge of the cover plate is embedded in a bead of caulking to prevent moisture penetration. The plywood cover plate must extend at least 75mm (3 in.) above grade (Figure 8.1). It is common practice for the cover plate to extend further up the wall, where it is lapped and protected by siding.

Protection of Corners

The CAN/CSA-S406 standard requires that the moisture barrier be protected at interior and exterior corners from mechanical damage that might occur during backfilling. Figure 8.2 details how interior and exterior corner protectors (e.g., treated plywood or gasket) should be assembled. Caulk the top and side edges of the corner protectors before applying them to the corners. The bottom edge should not be caulked. The protectors fit under the plywood cover strip and are held in place, on each side, by a single nail located 300mm (12 in.) from the top edge of the protector. The exposed nail heads should be caulked.

Figure 8.2
Inside and outside corner protection

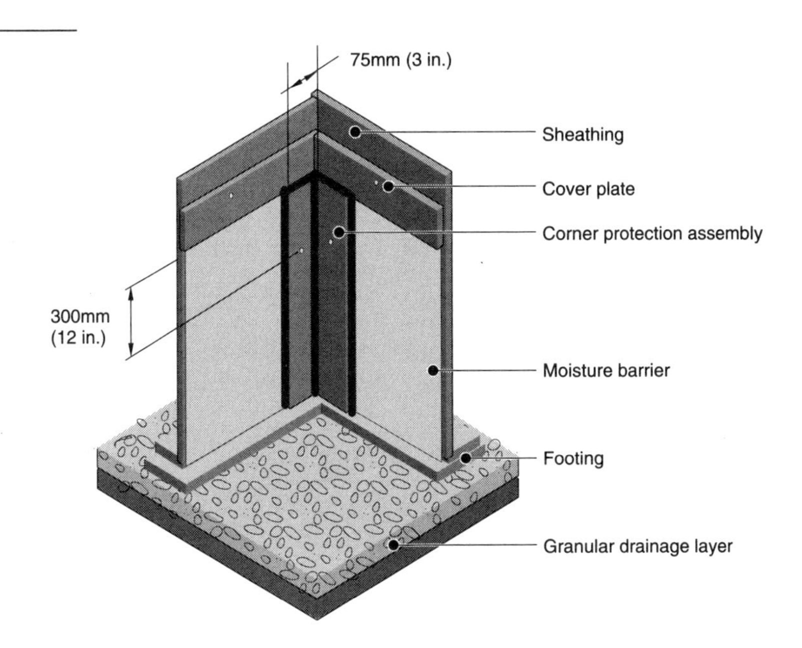

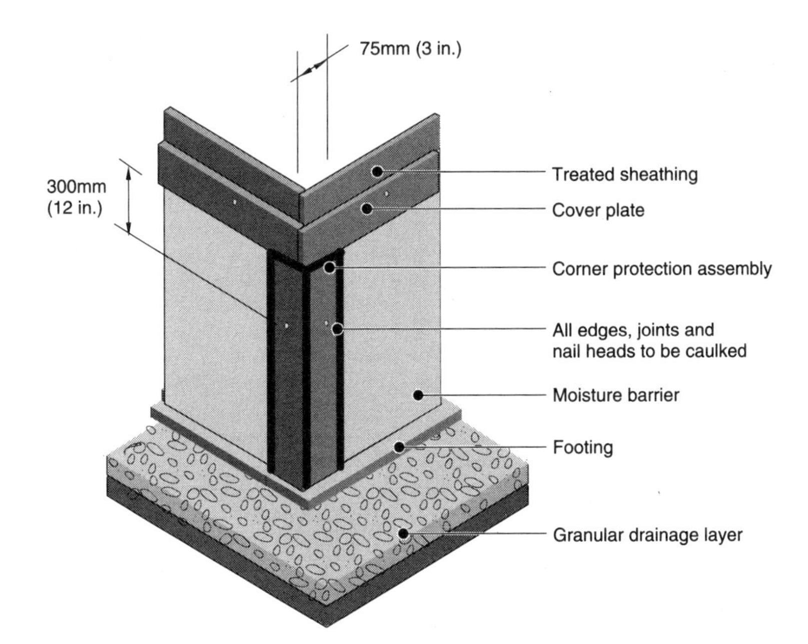

External Insulation

A standard 38 x 140mm (2 x 6 in.) PWF stud wall insulated with fibreglass batts between the studs has an R19 insulation value. This R value, adequate as it is for most climates, can be improved by adding rigid insulation to the exterior of the foundation. This is not a requirement of the CAN/CSA-S406 standard. The added costs must be weighed against the advantages.

Depending on the quality of the external insulation, heat loss can be reduced by an additional 10 to 20%. The insulation can also act as an extra moisture barrier and protect the polyethylene during backfilling.

Apart from its insulating qualities, the insulation should have high compressive strength and low water absorption. Two common materials used are extruded polystyrene and expanded bead polystyrene. Extruded polystyrene is more expensive but provides about 40% more insulating value and greater resistance to moisture.

There are also types of fibreglass insulation that are used below grade. This type of insulation enhances drainage around the wall.

Various fastening materials, such as 75mm (3 in.) galvanized nails with 19mm (3/4 in.) galvanized washers, are available from suppliers for attaching the rigid insulation to the foundation.

Above grade, the insulation should extend to the top of the foundation wall. Here it should be protected from exposure using treated plywood, two coats of portland-masonry cement parging on metal lath or other suitable materials. The protective covering should extend 300mm (12 in.) below grade and be attached by nailing through to the studs in the PWF (Figure 8.3).

Exterior siding should overlap the cover plate. If this is not possible, flashing should be installed where the siding and cover plate meet.

Following manufacturer's instructions, the insulation could extend to the full height of the building and covered with siding.

Figure 8.3
Applying external insulation

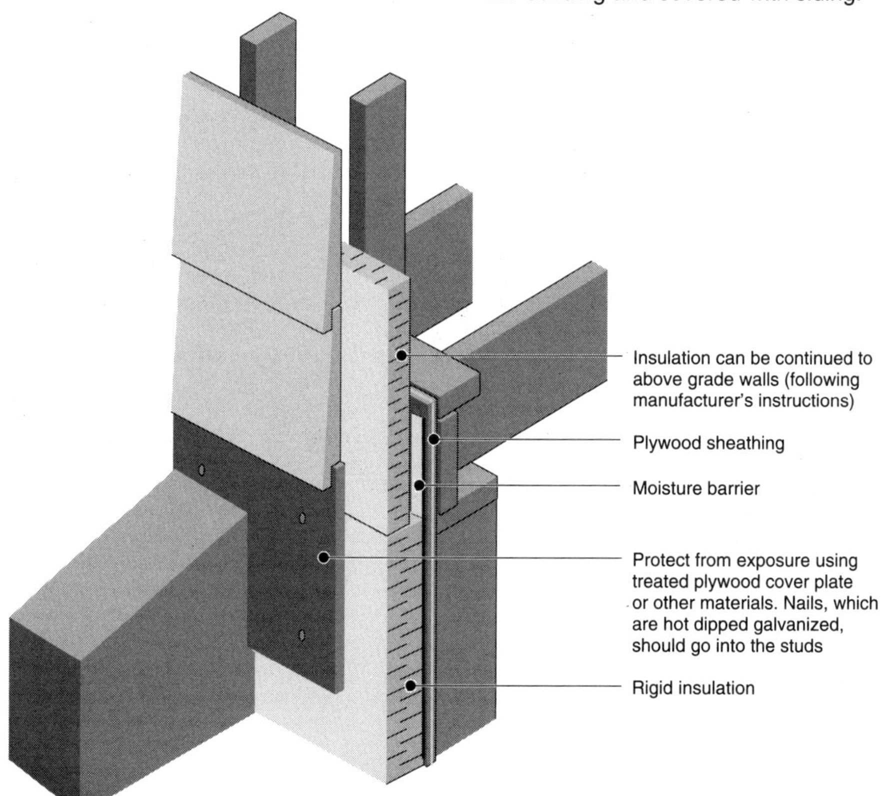

Backfilling

The choice of backfill material is important to the structural integrity and service life of any foundation. The type of material used affects the lateral load on the foundation. It provides the path through which water from the surrounding soil drains down into the granular drainage layer. Proper drainage prevents accumulation of ice (ice lensing) against the foundation and limits the possibility of damage to the foundation.

On sites where the native soil is free-draining and the water table is deep, the excavated material can be used for backfilling. On sites with poorly drained soils, backfilling with free-draining coarse sand or gravel will improve drainage. Table 8.1 gives the properties of backfill soils. Backfill material should be free of debris, frozen clumps and boulders larger than 150mm (6 in.) in diameter.

PWFs should not be backfilled until they have have been sealed and dampproofed, and have the top and bottom floors installed to resist lateral loads from the backfill. If either floor is not installed before backfilling, temporary bracing designed to resist the lateral backfill load must be provided.

Free-draining backfill should be placed uniformly around the building starting at the corners first to stabilize the structure; one side should not be backfilled completely before backfilling the opposite side. The plywood cover plate, as shown in Figure 8.1, makes a good guide for backfilling to the finish grade. Do not backfill with large pieces of earth, rock or frozen soil that could damage the moisture barrier.

Heavy equipment should be kept a safe distance away from the wall, generally a distance equal to the depth of the trench, to prevent excessive surcharge loads on the foundation wall. Machinery should be operated at right angles to the wall, not parallel to it.

The last 300mm (12 in.) should be backfilled with the native soil. In poor soil drainage conditions use of a manufactured drainage layer mat next to the foundation wall from grade to footing will assist drainage. The mat should have a vertical water permeability equal to coarse, clean sand and must be protected from infiltration of soil particles finer than fine sand.

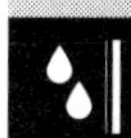

Table 8.1
Properties of backfill soils

Soil group	Description of backfill soil	Drainage characteristics	Frost heave potential	Soil volume change potential
Coarse grained (cohesionless)	clean sand and gravel	excellent	none	none
	sand and gravel	good to medium	medium	low
Fine grained (mostly cohesive)	clayey gravels clayey sands silty fine sands	medium	high	medium
	stiff residual silts and clays	medium	high	high
	very soft to soft clay silty clay organic silt and clay	poor	high	high
	medium to stiff clay deposited in chunks and protected from infiltration	poor	high	high

Site Grading

The major cause of leaking foundations, regardless of their type, is poor site drainage. As shown in Figure 8.4, sloping the grade away from the building at a minimum slope of 1 in 12 and providing swales will keep water from rainfall and snowmelt well away from the building. Directing roof water away from the building with eavestroughing and downspouts also greatly assists in keeping a basement dry. The adequacy of site drainage should be checked from time to time as settlement occurs.

Exterior Finishing

The above-grade portions of PWF walls can be finished in various ways. Vinyl or metal siding, prefinished wood siding, paint, stain, stucco or parging, as described for external insulation, may be used. Latex solid colour stains and paints are used on treated plywood as are oil-based semi-transparent stains though, in the latter instance, the finish colour may be affected by the green colour of the plywood.

Oil-base paints are not recommended for use on plywood. Preparing the plywood surfaces by cleaning with a wire brush helps the paint to better adhere to the surface.

Services

Penetrations for heating and mechanical services in the above-grade portions of PWF walls must be caulked or otherwise sealed to prevent rain penetration.

Figure 8.4
Drainage on building site

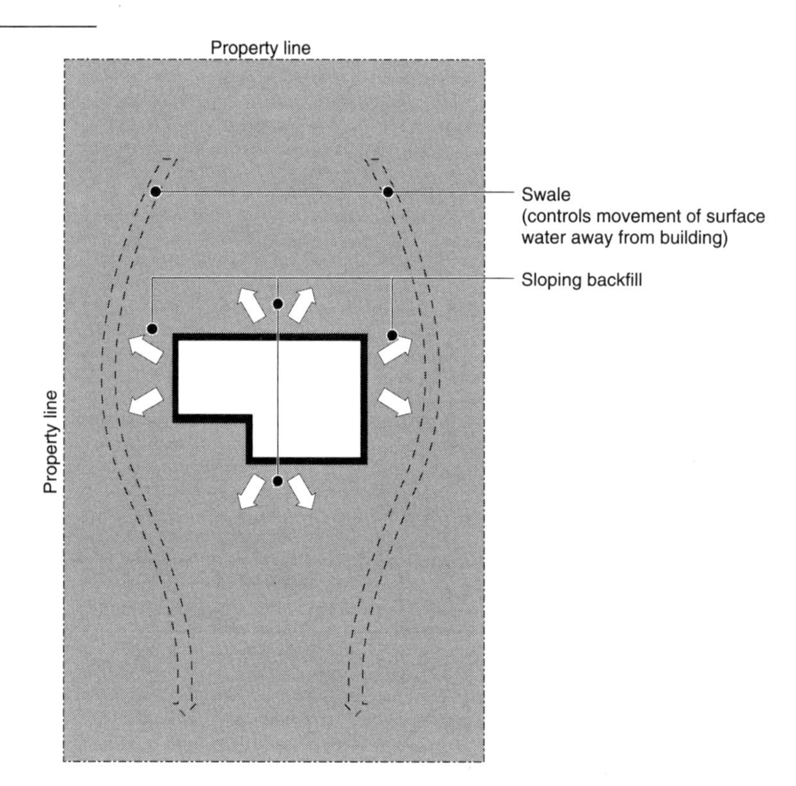

Interior Finishing

PWFs can be insulated and finished similarly to above grade rooms.

9.0 Interior Finishing

Insulating

Wood foundation walls can be easily and economically insulated to improve heating economy and warm living space in the basement. Batt-type insulation is installed between the studs and against the exterior sheathing to avoid circulation of cold air. A polyethylene vapour barrier is installed on the warm side of the insulation as in above grade walls.

The batt insulation is sometimes kept a few inches above the bottom plate to avoid wicking of any moisture that may occasionally be present. This practice will also allow escaping heat from the basement to prevent frost formation around the footings in relatively exposed conditions.

Where floor joists frame into the header at a side wall, the joist cavities should be filled with batt insulation and covered with polyethylene vapour barrier. In some house designs, such as high ranch-style bungalows, floor joists cantilever over the foundation. An air barrier should be installed to prevent cold air from entering the cantilevered space. (Note that cantilevers must be well attached to the foundation.) Heat outlets are installed in the basement ceiling so that warm air can circulate in the cantilevered joist cavities.

As for above ground walls, the perimeters of windows, doors and electrical boxes should be carefully sealed with polyethylene to prevent air exfiltration.

Wiring

Where electrical outlets are placed on exterior walls, the wiring should run vertically within a single stud space and pass through a hole drilled in the top plates between the floor joists. Wiring should then run along the wall through the suspended ceiling space or by drilling through the joists.

Heating and Ventilation

Heating and ventilation ducts should be installed so that studs, top plates, blocking and framing anchors are not cut, notched or removed. One solution is to frame in wall or ceiling chases next to the foundation wall for routing ductwork.

Finishing

When finishing the inside of a PWF, a polyethylene vapour barrier is placed over the insulated wall as is normal for all types of construction. Ensuring that the inside vapour barrier is sound and free from rips will prevent condensation in the wall cavity.

Ceilings and walls of a PWF can be finished with any of the common materials. The wood frame walls of the PWF make this a relatively simple operation without consuming floor area as would be the case with other types of foundations that require interior wood frame walls to be built before finishing.

Ceiling height should be planned before construction. If high ceilings are desired in the basement, use 3m (10 ft.) studs.

Indoor Air Quality

In a 1992 study, *Air Tightness and Air Quality in Preserved Wood Foundations*, by the Canada Mortgage and Housing Corporation (CMHC), thirteen PWF homes built between 1981 and 1991 were tested for indoor air quality.

Two potential sources of air pollutants were examined: soil gas and off-gassing of the chemical preservatives in the wood. Soil gases can enter basements through cracks and holes in the air vapour barrier, hence the desire to construct air tight basements.

Air samples were taken in the basement living area, inside wall cavities and under sleeper floors. The PWFs were found to be tightly constructed. Air leakage occurred at locations not directly associated with PWF construction such as at headers and windows.

The researchers sampled and analyzed air in the wall cavity for volatile organic compounds. They found that levels of chemicals were very low and well under the regulatory guidelines of the Ontario Ministry of the Environment for ambient air quality. Air quality in the PWF homes compared favourably to that of a home with a concrete foundation.

The study confirms that PWFs, built according to the CSA standard, offer homeowners a high level of air quality in addition to warm, dry living space.

Methods of preventing soil gas infiltration in basements are reviewed in the Appendix of the 1990 NBCC.

Special Topics

Frost wall constructed to support a porch.

10.0 Special Topics

Attached Garages

Where driveway or garage floor slabs supporting cars or light trucks abut the foundation wall, as occurs with attached garages and carports, higher than normal loads are exerted on the adjacent foundation wall. Whether using asphalt or a concrete slab, the foundation wall next to the garage floor must be strengthened by selecting the stud sizes and spacings for a backfill height 500mm (20 in.) greater than the actual backfill height, or the slab can be supported around its perimeter by a preserved wood knee wall placed next to the foundation wall in a manner similar to that for supporting brick veneer (Figure 10.2).

The PWF walls of the garage are usually placed in a trench and backfilled on both sides, without excavating the entire floor area of the garage. In backfilling, it should be expected that there will be some differential settlement between the excavated and unexcavated areas. This can be minimized by taking care in backfilling, by adding concrete to the backfill mixture or by reinforcing the slab.

Footing plates should be located below the level of frost penetration on 150mm (6 in.) of granular drainage material deposited at the bottom of the trench. Generally, footings need not be below frost where the garage is heated, although this depends on local soil conditions. As mentioned in Chapter 5, the trenched footings must be drained if there is likelihood of water accumulation and subsequent frost heaving.

Where PWF walls supporting garages are backfilled to about the same level on both sides, the studs may be 38 x 89mm (2 x 4 in.) and the plywood sheathing 12.5mm (1/2 in.) in thickness. The plywood sheathing need extend only half way down the wall since its purpose is to provide rigidity during construction and to act as a substrate for finishing the above-grade portion of the wall. Walls should be braced to maintain their alignment during backfill.

Typically, full panels of treated plywood sheathing are nailed horizontally to the wall studs. Only one width of sheathing is necessary, the studs farther down being left exposed.

Figure 10.1
Garage attachment and two methods of support for concrete slab

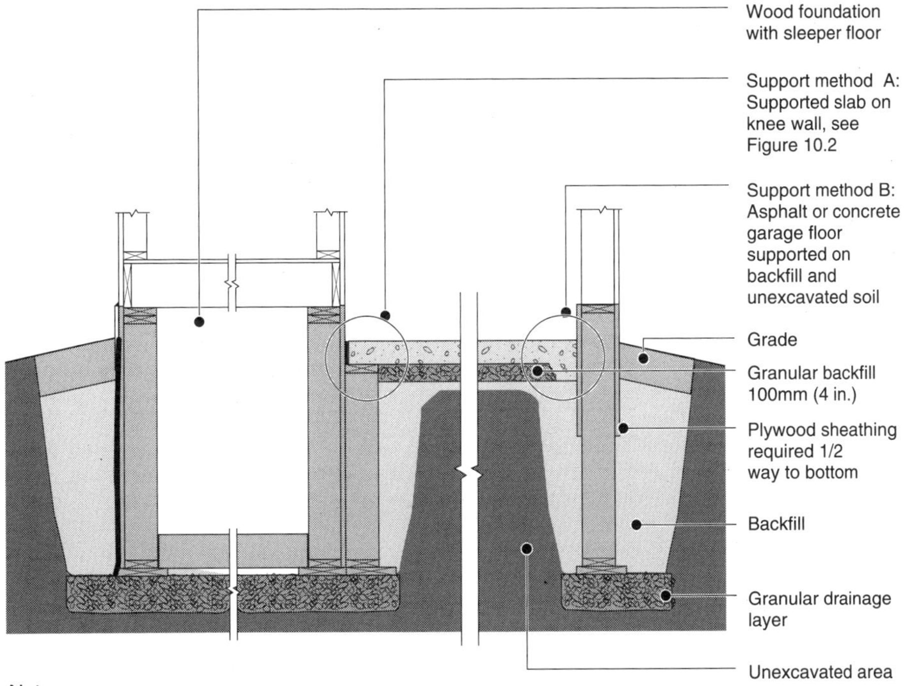

Note:
1. Slab should be supported using method A or method B. These methods should not be used together.

The PWF wall should also run beneath the door opening but will need to be shorter to accommodate the thickness of the slab. To strengthen the threshold, it may be necessary to use a built-up top plate (Figure 10.3).

Detached Garages

Detached garages are constructed in a similar manner to attached garages, with trenches dug for the PWF walls instead of

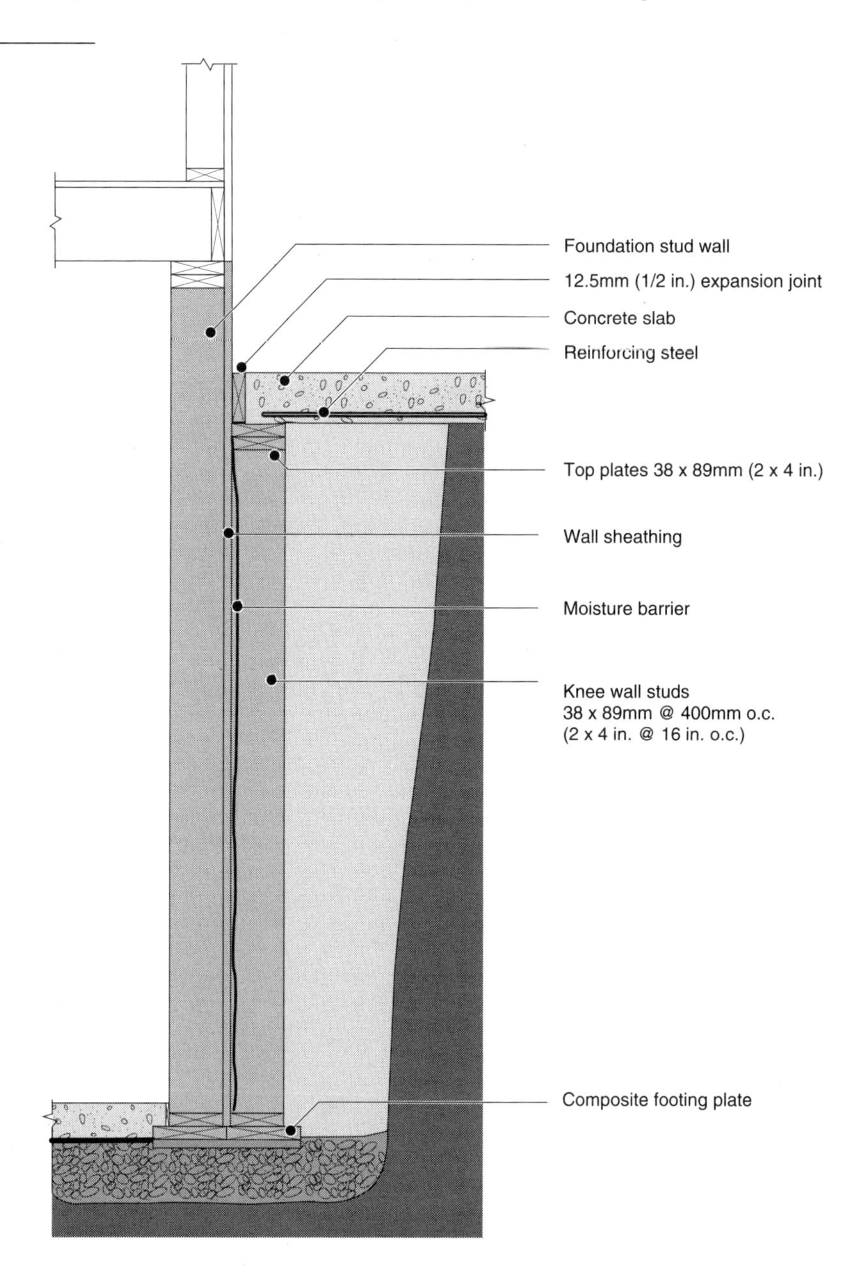

Figure 10.2
Knee wall support for concrete slab, porch or steps at building

a complete excavation. Sometimes detached garages are built on floating footings which negates the need for foundation walls. The local building authority can usually advise on the most appropriate building method for a specific area.

Exterior Steps and Porches

Exterior steps and porches can be supported at one end on a knee wall next to the main PWF foundation and at the other end by a treated wood stud wall backfilled on both sides, or by other suitable means.

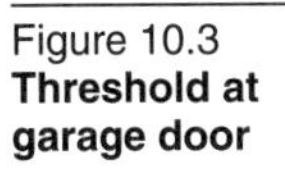

Figure 10.3
Threshold at garage door

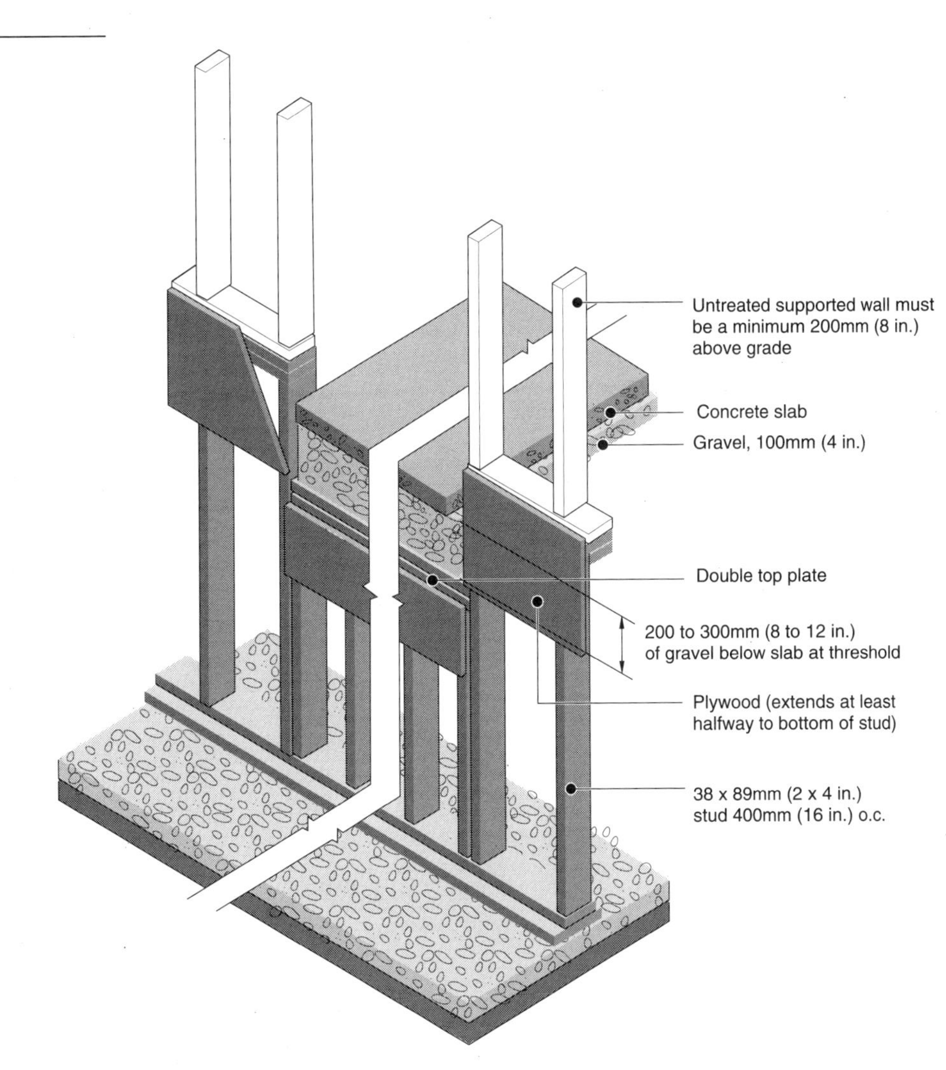

Crawl Spaces

Partially excavated and unexcavated crawl spaces are used where it is not possible or desirable to build full basements, such as in split-level houses or on rocky or wet sites (Figure 10.4).

Trenches are excavated to below the level of frost penetration and a 125mm (5 in.) layer of gravel placed in the trenches and compacted as a base for the wood footings. Footing sizes are the same as for full basements.

Figure 10.4
Partially excavated and unexcavated crawl spaces

Partially excavated crawl space

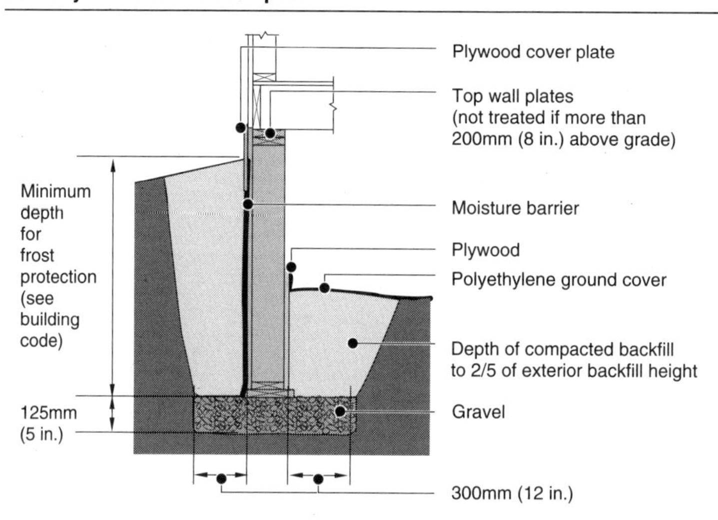

Unexcavated crawl space with trenched footing

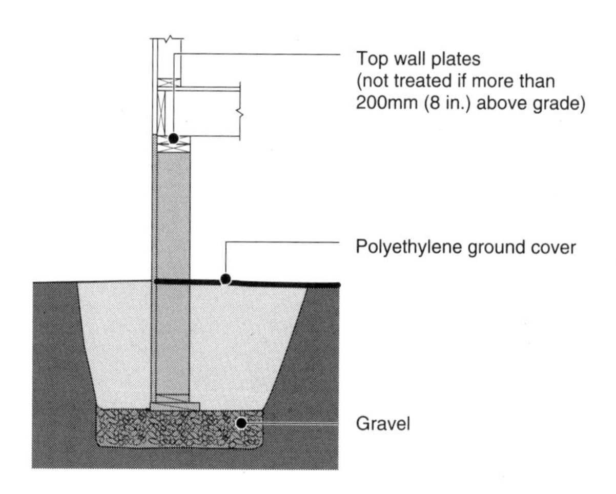

Notes:
1. Polyethylene moisture barriers shall not extend under exterior footing plate or between the granular drainage layer and the backfill at the exterior wall.
2. Restraint at base of wall is provided by unexcavated soil inside; load transfer is through compacted soil backfill inside wall footing.
3. Ventilation of enclosed crawl space is required unless crawl space is heated.

Figure 10.5
Insulated wall of unexcavated crawl space

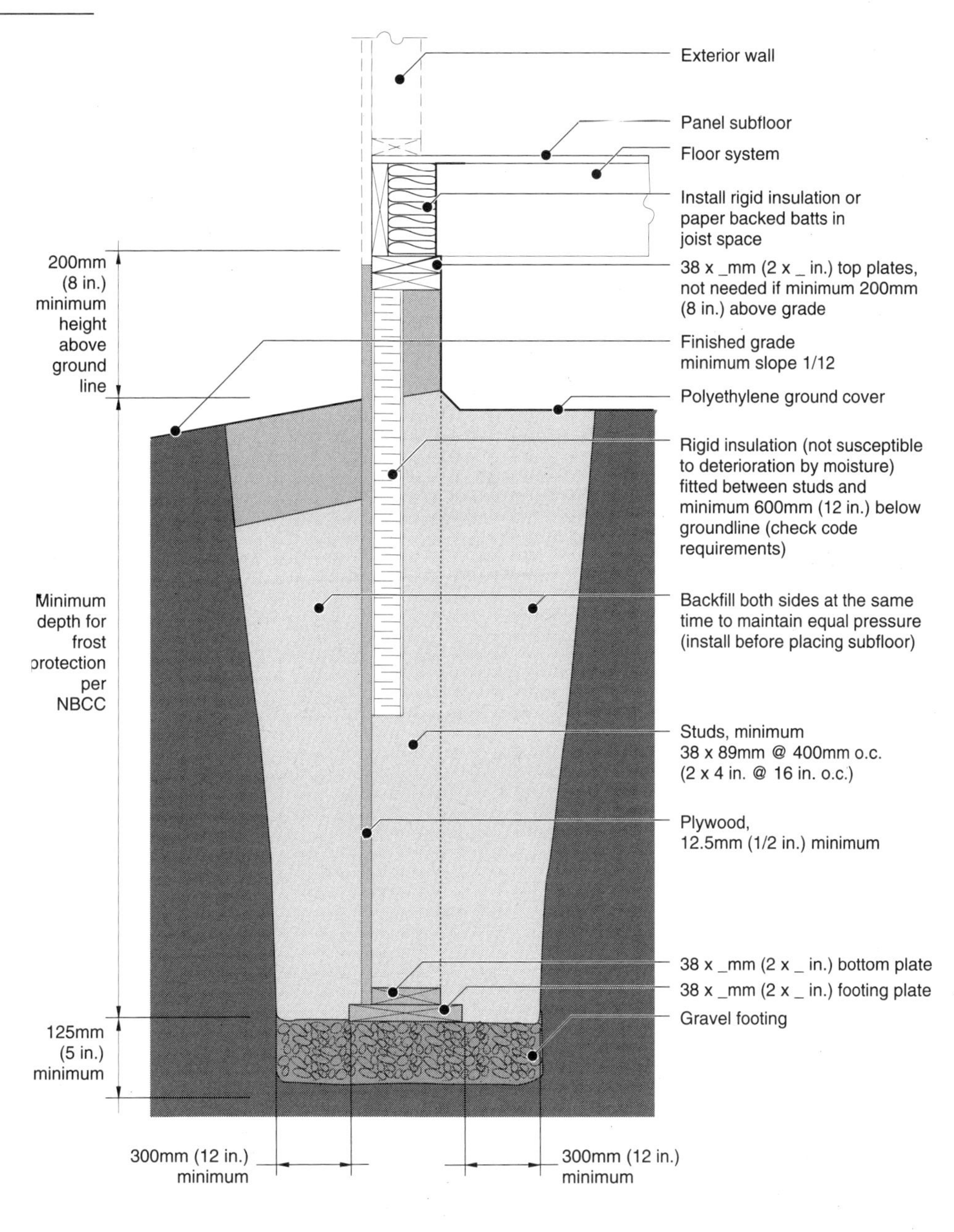

Notes:
1. Ventilation of enclosed crawl spaces is required.
2. Because grade inside is not lower than outside, the drainage system and exterior moisture protection (polyethylene) is optional (depends on site).
3. Observe minimum interior clearance of 300mm (12 in.) between floor joists and ground or 600mm (24 in.) if service lines are installed.
4. Insulate crawl space wall or floor above as required; drawing shows minimum wall insulation.
5. Normal stud requirements and normal nailing schedule for joist ends are used because soil loads are balanced.

The walls are placed in trenches and, in the case of unexcavated crawl spaces, both sides are backfilled to the level of the outside grade to provide lateral support. For partially excavated crawl spaces the depth of the interior backfill should be at least 2/5 of the exterior backfill height. If less than 2/5 backfill is used, some means must be provided to give lateral resistance at the bottom of the wall.

Again, as described in Chapter 5, the trenched footings should be drained if water accumulation causing frost heave could occur. If a sump pit is necessary, the granular drainage layer below the trenched footings should be sloped to drain to the sump connected to a sewer, ditch or dry well. The ground in the crawl space should be completely covered with polyethylene with the joints lapped not less than 100mm (4 in.) and weighed down with sand or other suitable material (Figure 10.6).

The crawl space walls and ground floor are framed using methods already described. There should be a minimum clearance of 300mm (12 in.) between the ground and the framing members of the ground floor. Increase this distance to 600mm (24 in.) if service lines are to be installed.

The underside of crawl space floors and mechanical installations under the floor should be insulated unless the crawl space is heated. If unheated, the crawl space must be ventilated as prescribed in building codes.Insulating the crawl space walls with rigid insulation, as shown in Figure 10.5, will help to lower energy costs.

As with all foundations, the site should be graded to encourage drainage away from the building and normal procedures followed for access, ventilation, clearances and fire protection as prescribed in building codes.

Figure 10.6 **Crawl space drainage of trenched footings**

Plan

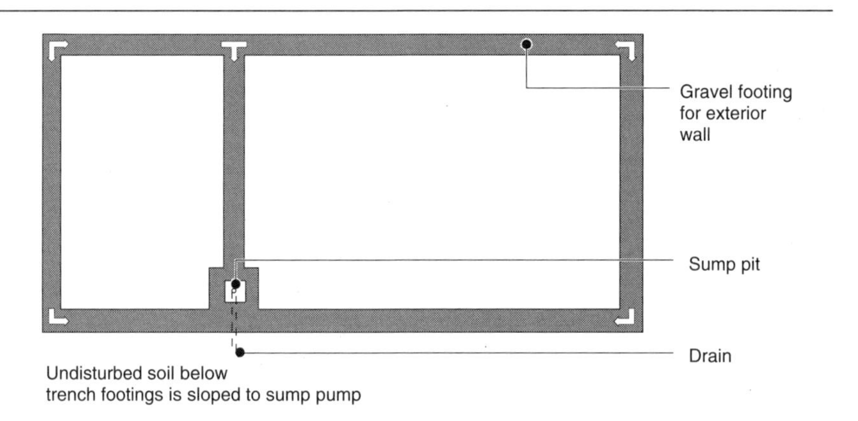

Section

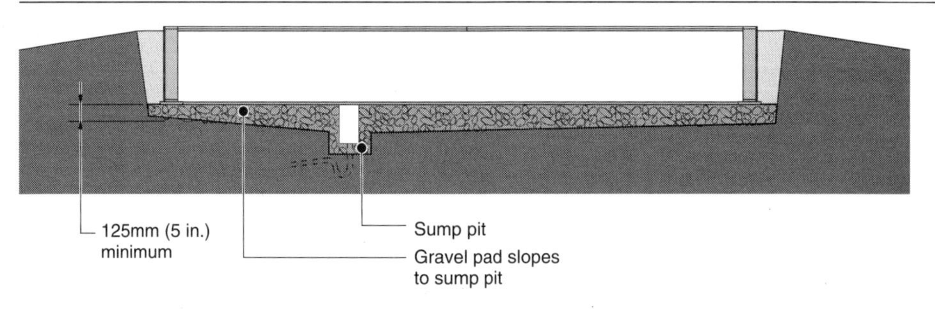

Walk-out Basements

Foundations built into hills are often constructed as walk-out basements with little or no backfill on one side and high backfill on the other side. As already discussed in Chapter 7, the end walls must be strengthened with increased nailing to provide resistance to racking loads. Alternatively, interior shearwalls may be designed to provide resistance.

The exposed wall with the doorway to the exterior should rest on a frost wall extending below frost penetration (Figure 10.7). Both sides of the door opening should be framed with double full-length wall studs. Openings wider than 3.6m (12 ft.) should be framed with triple full-length studs on either side.

Figure 10.7
Frost wall in walk-out basements (typical detail)

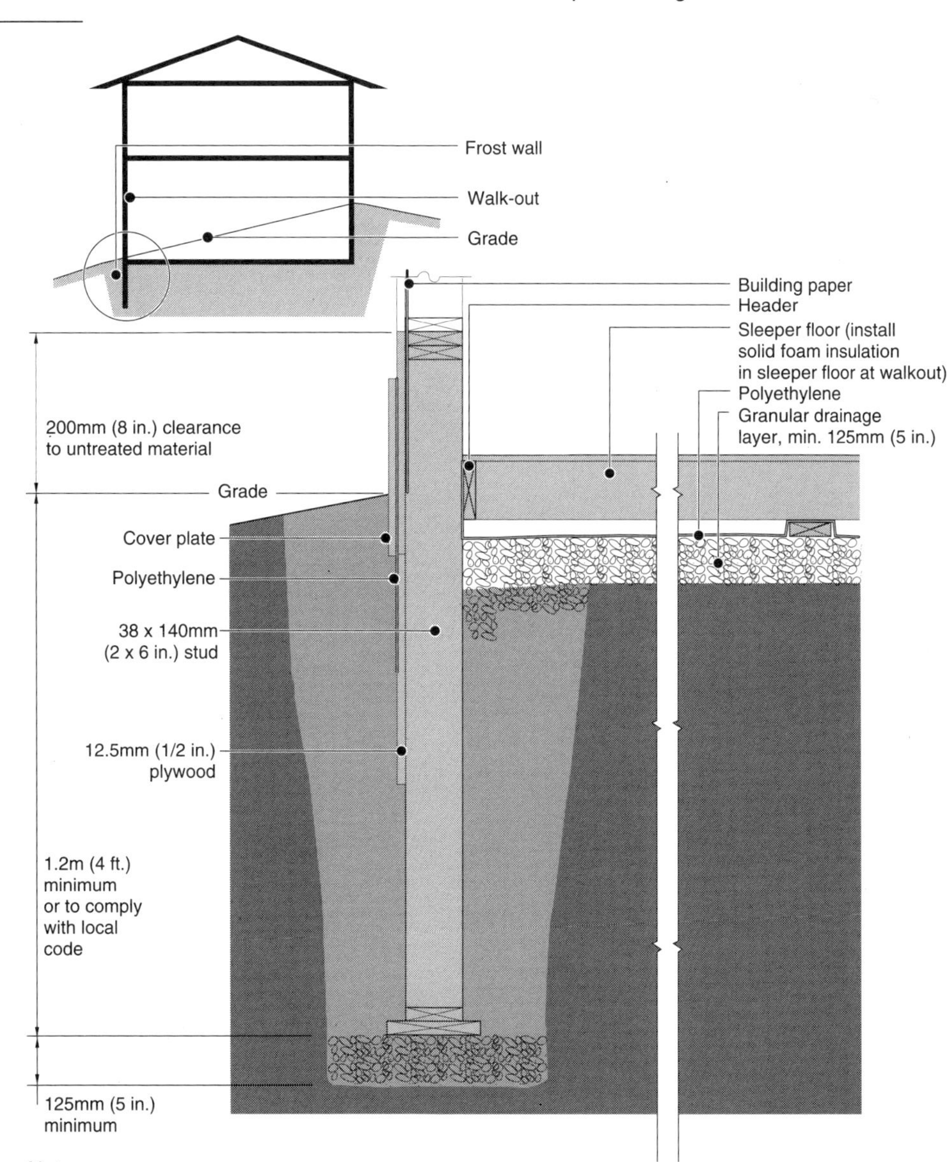

Notes:
1. Could use 3.6m (12 ft.) studs that are continuous from footing to top of above-grade wall.
2. This detail should be checked by a qualified engineer when L/W ratio of the house is high (see chapter 7) or in some soils, such as certain clays, that exert excessive lateral loads when wet.

PWF Additions

A PWF addition is an economical way of increasing living space and value of the home. It is usually faster and more convenient to build in built-up areas and easier to finish inside.

A PWF addition to an existing foundation is constructed in a similar manner to that of a regular PWF. The condition of the present basement and its drainage should be examined for moisture problems or blocked drainage tiles.

The 125mm (5 in.) granular drainage layer is distributed over the excavation and lightly tamped. The excavation can be sloped so that drainage runs into the existing tiles, or a sump pit with separate drainage may be required. Previous experience with drainage around the basement may guide this decision.

The PWF addition must be thoroughly sealed to the old foundation to prevent water infiltration. Detail A of Figure 10.8 shows a flush corner where the foundations are aligned. The stud of the adjacent

Figure 10.8
Attaching a PWF add-on, detail A

Plan

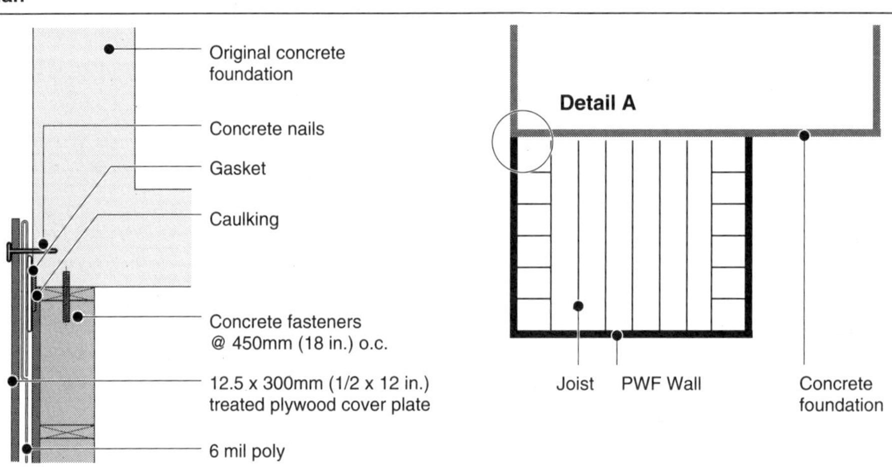

Isometric

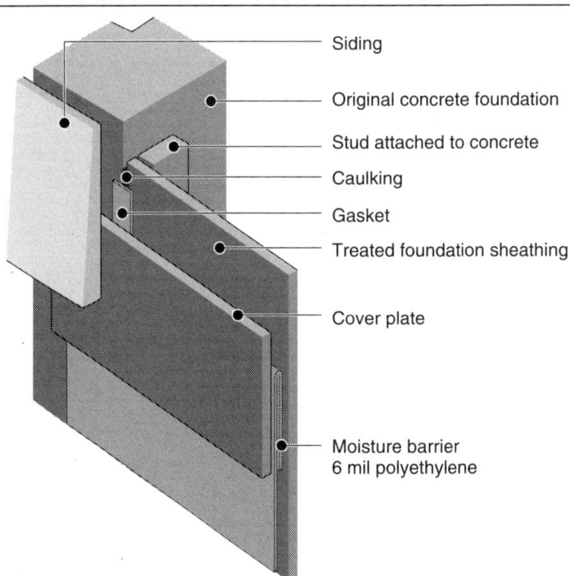

PWF wall panel is caulked along its flat face and then attached to the existing foundation with concrete fasteners.

Protective materials are layered over the joint. Then a waterproof gasket, either metal flashing, vinyl, rubber strip gaskets or waterproof tape, is pressed into the caulking. Polyethylene is lapped over the joint for the entire height of the wall. The treated plywood cover strip is then applied at grade level.

The same idea of layering applies to Detail B where foundations intersect to form an interior corner. The first PWF wall stud is attached to the existing foundation as described in Detail A. A bead of caulking is placed at the intersection of the new and old walls. A gasket, folded to fit the interior corner, is pressed into the caulking and then covered by the polyethylene moisture barrier and treated plywood cover strip.

Figure 10.9
Attaching a PWF add-on, detail B

Plan

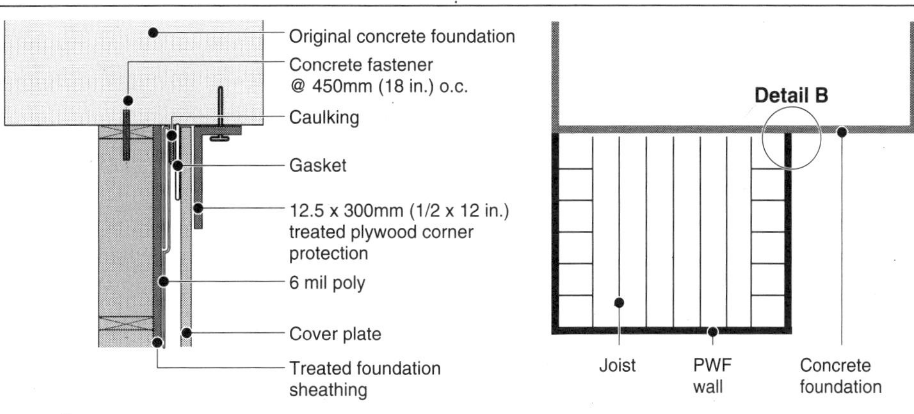

Isometric

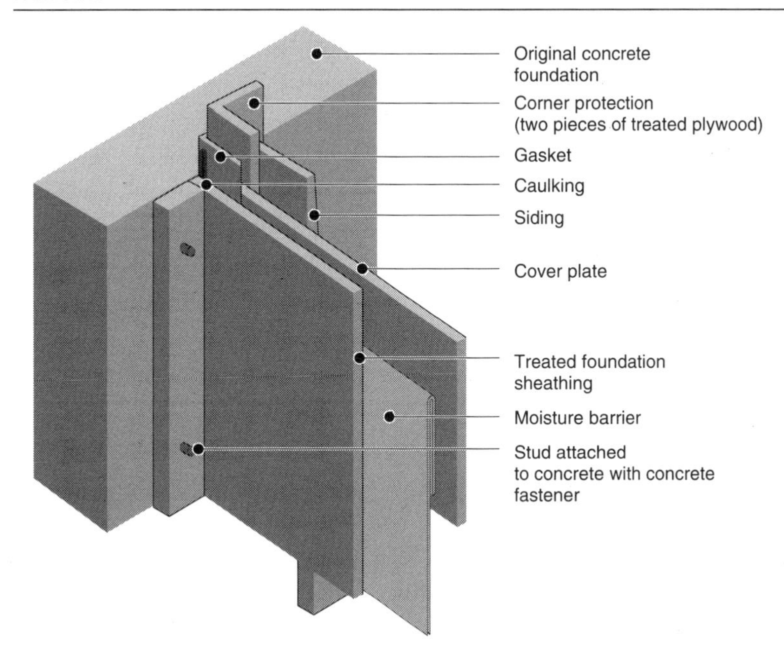

Appendix

PWF Stud Selection Tables

A.1 Suspended Wood Floor

3.0m 400mm

Stud length = 3.0m (10 ft.)
Stud spacing = 400mm (16 in.)

Vertical load range kN/m (plf)	Species	Grade	Backfill height, m (ft.-in.) 1.2 (4-0)	1.5 (5-0)	1.8 (6-0)	2.1 (7-0)	2.4 (8-0)	2.6 (8-6)	2.7 (9-0)	2.9 (9-6)
15 (1030)	Group 1	Sel Str	4	4	4	6	6	6	8	10
to	Group 1	No. 1/No. 2	4	6	6	6	8	8	8	10
20 (1370)	Group 2	Sel Str	6	6	6	6	8	8	8	10
	Group 2	No. 1/No. 2	6	6	6	6	8	10	10	n/a
20.1 (1375)	Group 1	Sel Str	4	4	6	6	6	6	8	10
to	Group 1	No. 1/No. 2	6	6	6	6	8	8	10	10
25 (1715)	Group 2	Sel Str	6	6	6	6	8	8	8	10
	Group 2	No. 1/No. 2	6	6	6	6	8	10	10	n/a
25.1 (1720)	Group 1	Sel Str	4	6	6	6	6	6	8	10
to	Group 1	No. 1/No. 2	6	6	6	6	8	8	10	10
30 (2055)	Group 2	Sel Str	6	6	6	6	8	8	10	10
	Group 2	No. 1/No. 2	6	6	6	8	10	10	10	n/a
30.1 (2060)	Group 1	Sel Str	6	6	6	6	6	6	8	10
to	Group 1	No. 1/No. 2	6	6	6	6	8	8	10	10
35 (2400)	Group 2	Sel Str	6	6	6	6	8	8	10	10
	Group 2	No. 1/No. 2	6	6	6	8	10	10	10	n/a
35.1 (2405)	Group 1	Sel Str	6	6	6	6	6	8	8	10
to	Group 1	No. 1/No. 2	6	6	6	6	8	8	10	10
40 (2740)	Group 2	Sel Str	6	6	6	6	8	8	10	10
	Group 2	No. 1/No. 2	6	6	6	8	10	10	10	n/a
40.1 (2750)	Group 1	Sel Str	6	6	6	6	6	8	8	10
to	Group 1	No. 1/No. 2	6	6	6	6	8	8	10	10
45 (3085)	Group 2	Sel Str	6	6	6	6	8	8	10	10
	Group 2	No. 1/No. 2	6	6	8	8	10	10	n/a	n/a
45.1 (3090)	Group 1	Sel Str	6	6	6	6	6	8	8	10
to	Group 1	No. 1/No. 2	6	6	6	6	8	10	10	10
50 (3425)	Group 2	Sel Str	6	6	6	6	8	10	10	10
	Group 2	No. 1/No. 2	6	6	8	8	10	10	n/a	n/a

Notes:
1. 4 is a 38 x 89mm stud (2 x 4 in.)
2. 6 is a 38 x 140mm stud (2 x 6 in.)
3. 8 is a 38 x 184mm stud (2 x 8 in.)
4. 10 is a 38 x 235mm stud (2 x 10 in.)
5. Species Group 1 is S-P-F, D.Fir-L, Hem-Fir
6. Species Group 2 is Northern Species Group
7. For the above calculations a suspended joist depth of 200mm (8 in.) and a cantilever length of 500mm (20 in.) was assumed.

PWF Stud Selection Tables

3.0m 300mm

Suspended Wood Floor

Stud length = 3.0m (10 ft.)
Stud spacing = 300mm (12 in.)

Vertical load range kN/m (plf)	Species	Grade	Backfill height, m (ft.-in.) 1.2 (4-0)	1.5 (5-0)	1.8 (6-0)	2.1 (7-0)	2.4 (8-0)	2.6 (8-6)	2.7 (9-0)	2.9 (9-6)
15 (1030)	Group 1	Sel Str	4	4	4	6	6	6	6	6
to	Group 1	No. 1/No. 2	4	4	4	6	6	6	8	8
20 (1370)	Group 2	Sel Str	4	4	6	6	6	6	8	8
	Group 2	No. 1/No. 2	4	6	6	6	8	8	8	10
20.1 (1375)	Group 1	Sel Str	4	4	4	6	6	6	6	6
to	Group 1	No. 1/No. 2	4	4	6	6	6	6	8	8
25 (1715)	Group 2	Sel Str	4	4	6	6	6	6	8	8
	Group 2	No. 1/No. 2	6	6	6	6	8	8	10	10
25.1 (1720)	Group 1	Sel Str	4	4	4	6	6	6	6	6
to	Group 1	No. 1/No. 2	4	6	6	6	6	8	8	8
30 (2055)	Group 2	Sel Str	4	6	6	6	6	8	8	8
	Group 2	No. 1/No. 2	6	6	6	6	8	8	10	10
30.1 (2060)	Group 1	Sel Str	4	4	4	6	6	6	6	6
to	Group 1	No. 1/No. 2	4	6	6	6	6	8	8	8
35 (2400)	Group 2	Sel Str	6	6	6	6	6	8	8	8
	Group 2	No. 1/No. 2	6	6	6	6	8	8	10	10
35.1 (2405)	Group 1	Sel Str	4	4	6	6	6	6	6	6
to	Group 1	No. 1/No. 2	6	6	6	6	6	8	8	8
40 (2740)	Group 2	Sel Str	6	6	6	6	6	8	8	8
	Group 2	No. 1/No. 2	6	6	6	6	8	8	10	10
40.1 (2750)	Group 1	Sel Str	4	6	6	6	6	6	6	6
to	Group 1	No. 1/No. 2	6	6	6	6	6	8	8	8
45 (3085)	Group 2	Sel Str	6	6	6	6	6	8	8	8
	Group 2	No. 1/No. 2	6	6	6	6	8	8	10	10
45.1 (3090)	Group 1	Sel Str	6	6	6	6	6	6	6	8
to	Group 1	No. 1/No. 2	6	6	6	6	6	8	8	8
50 (3425)	Group 2	Sel Str	6	6	6	6	8	8	8	8
	Group 2	No. 1/No. 2	6	6	6	6	8	10	10	10

Notes:
1. 4 is a 38 x 89mm stud (2 x 4 in.)
2. 6 is a 38 x 140mm stud (2 x 6 in.)
3. 8 is a 38 x 184mm stud (2 x 8 in.)
4. 10 is a 38 x 235mm stud (2 x 10 in.)
5. Species Group 1 is S-P-F, D.Fir-L, Hem-Fir
6. Species Group 2 is Northern Species Group
7. For the above calculations a suspended joist depth of 200mm (8 in.) and a cantilever length of 500mm (20 in.) was assumed.

PWF Stud Selection Tables

Suspended Wood Floor

3.0m 200mm

Stud length = 3.0m (10 ft.)
Stud spacing = 200mm (8 in.)

Vertical load range kN/m (plf)	Species	Grade	Backfill height, m (ft.-in.) 1.2 (4-0)	1.5 (5-0)	1.8 (6-0)	2.1 (7-0)	2.4 (8-0)	2.6 (8-6)	2.7 (9-0)	2.9 (9-6)
15 (1030)	Group 1	Sel Str	4	4	4	4	6	6	6	6
to	Group 1	No. 1/No. 2	4	4	4	4	6	6	6	6
20 (1370)	Group 2	Sel Str	4	4	4	4	6	6	6	6
	Group 2	No. 1/No. 2	4	4	4	6	6	6	6	8
20.1 (1375)	Group 1	Sel Str	4	4	4	4	6	6	6	6
to	Group 1	No. 1/No. 2	4	4	4	4	6	6	6	6
25 (1715)	Group 2	Sel Str	4	4	4	4	6	6	6	6
	Group 2	No. 1/No. 2	4	4	4	6	6	6	8	8
25.1 (1720)	Group 1	Sel Str	4	4	4	4	6	6	6	6
to	Group 1	No. 1/No. 2	4	4	4	4	6	6	6	6
30 (2055)	Group 2	Sel Str	4	4	4	4	6	6	6	6
	Group 2	No. 1/No. 2	4	4	6	6	6	6	8	8
30.1 (2060)	Group 1	Sel Str	4	4	4	4	6	6	6	6
to	Group 1	No. 1/No. 2	4	4	4	4	6	6	6	6
35 (2400)	Group 2	Sel Str	4	4	4	6	6	6	6	6
	Group 2	No. 1/No. 2	4	4	6	6	6	6	8	8
35.1 (2405)	Group 1	Sel Str	4	4	4	4	6	6	6	6
to	Group 1	No. 1/No. 2	4	4	4	6	6	6	6	6
40 (2740)	Group 2	Sel Str	4	4	4	6	6	6	6	6
	Group 2	No. 1/No. 2	4	6	6	6	6	6	8	8
40.1 (2750)	Group 1	Sel Str	4	4	4	4	6	6	6	6
to	Group 1	No. 1/No. 2	4	4	4	6	6	6	6	6
45 (3085)	Group 2	Sel Str	4	4	4	6	6	6	6	6
	Group 2	No. 1/No. 2	6	6	6	6	6	6	8	8
45.1 (3090)	Group 1	Sel Str	4	4	4	4	6	6	6	6
to	Group 1	No. 1/No. 2	4	4	4	6	6	6	6	6
50 (3425)	Group 2	Sel Str	4	4	6	6	6	6	6	6
	Group 2	No. 1/No. 2	6	6	6	6	6	8	8	8

Notes:
1. 4 is a 38 x 89mm stud (2 x 4 in.)
2. 6 is a 38 x 140mm stud (2 x 6 in.)
3. 8 is a 38 x 184mm stud (2 x 8 in.)
4. 10 is a 38 x 235mm stud (2 x 10 in.)
5. Species Group 1 is S-P-F, D.Fir-L, Hem-Fir
6. Species Group 2 is Northern Species Group
7. For the above calculations a suspended joist depth of 200mm (8 in.) and a cantilever length of 500mm (20 in.) was assumed.

PWF Stud Selection Tables

3.6m 400mm

Suspended Wood Floor

Stud length = 3.6m (12 ft.)
Stud spacing = 400mm (16 in.)

Vertical load range kN/m (plf)	Species	Grade	Backfill height, m (ft.-in.) 1.5 (5-0)	1.8 (6-0)	2.1 (7-0)	2.4 (8-0)	2.7 (9-0)
15 (1030)	Group 1	Sel Str	6	6	6	6	8
to	Group 1	No. 1/No. 2	6	6	6	8	10
20 (1370)	Group 2	Sel Str	6	6	6	8	10
	Group 2	No. 1/No. 2	6	6	8	10	n/a
20.1 (1375)	Group 1	Sel Str	6	6	6	6	8
to	Group 1	No. 1/No. 2	6	6	6	8	10
25 (1715)	Group 2	Sel Str	6	6	6	8	10
	Group 2	No. 1/No. 2	6	6	8	10	n/a
25.1 (1720)	Group 1	Sel Str	6	6	6	6	8
to	Group 1	No. 1/No. 2	6	6	6	8	10
30 (2055)	Group 2	Sel Str	6	6	6	8	10
	Group 2	No. 1/No. 2	6	6	8	10	n/a
30.1 (2060)	Group 1	Sel Str	6	6	6	8	8
to	Group 1	No. 1/No. 2	6	6	6	8	10
35 (2400)	Group 2	Sel Str	6	6	8	8	10
	Group 2	No. 1/No. 2	6	8	8	10	n/a
35.1 (2405)	Group 1	Sel Str	6	6	6	8	8
to	Group 1	No. 1/No. 2	6	6	8	8	10
40 (2740)	Group 2	Sel Str	6	6	8	8	10
	Group 2	No. 1/No. 2	6	8	8	10	n/a
40.1 (2750)	Group 1	Sel Str	6	6	6	8	8
to	Group 1	No. 1/No. 2	6	6	8	8	10
45 (3085)	Group 2	Sel Str	6	6	8	10	10
	Group 2	No. 1/No. 2	8	8	8	10	n/a
45.1 (3090)	Group 1	Sel Str	6	6	6	8	8
to	Group 1	No. 1/No. 2	6	6	8	10	10
50 (3425)	Group 2	Sel Str	6	6	8	10	10
	Group 2	No. 1/No. 2	8	8	8	10	n/a

Notes:
1. 4 is a 38 x 89mm stud (2 x 4 in.)
2. 6 is a 38 x 140mm stud (2 x 6 in.)
3. 8 is a 38 x 184mm stud (2 x 8 in.)
4. 10 is a 38 x 235mm stud (2 x 10 in.)
5. Species Group 1 is S-P-F, D.Fir-L, Hem-Fir
6. Species Group 2 is Northern Species Group
7. For the above calculations a suspended joist depth of 200mm (8 in.) and a cantilever length of 500mm (20 in.) was assumed.

PWF Stud Selection Tables

Suspended Wood Floor

3.6m 300mm

Stud length = 3.6 m (12 ft.)
Stud spacing = 300mm (12 in.)

Vertical load range kN/m (plf)	Species	Grade	Backfill height, m (ft.-in.) 1.8 (6-0)	2.1 (7-0)	2.4 (8-0)	2.7 (9-0)	3 (10-0)	3.2 (10-6)	3.3 (11-0)
15 (1030)	Group 1	Sel Str	4	6	6	8	8	10	10
to	Group 1	No. 1/No. 2	6	6	6	8	10	10	n/a
20 (1370)	Group 2	Sel Str	6	6	6	8	10	10	10
	Group 2	No. 1/No. 2	6	6	8	10	n/a	n/a	n/a
20.1 (1375)	Group 1	Sel Str	6	6	6	8	8	10	10
to	Group 1	No. 1/No. 2	6	6	8	8	10	10	n/a
25 (1715)	Group 2	Sel Str	6	6	8	8	10	10	n/a
	Group 2	No. 1/No. 2	6	6	8	10	n/a	n/a	n/a
25.1 (1720)	Group 1	Sel Str	6	6	6	8	8	10	10
to	Group 1	No. 1/No. 2	6	6	8	8	10	10	n/a
30 (2055)	Group 2	Sel Str	6	6	8	8	10	10	n/a
	Group 2	No. 1/No. 2	6	6	8	10	n/a	n/a	n/a
30.1 (2060)	Group 1	Sel Str	6	6	6	8	8	10	10
to	Group 1	No. 1/No. 2	6	6	8	8	10	10	n/a
35 (2400)	Group 2	Sel Str	6	6	8	8	10	10	n/a
	Group 2	No. 1/No. 2	6	8	8	10	n/a	n/a	n/a
35.1 (2405)	Group 1	Sel Str	6	6	6	8	8	10	10
to	Group 1	No. 1/No. 2	6	6	8	10	10	10	n/a
40 (2740)	Group 2	Sel Str	6	6	8	8	10	10	n/a
	Group 2	No. 1/No. 2	6	8	8	10	n/a	n/a	n/a
40.1 (2750)	Group 1	Sel Str	6	6	6	8	8	10	10
to	Group 1	No. 1/No. 2	6	6	8	10	10	n/a	n/a
45 (3085)	Group 2	Sel Str	6	6	8	10	10	10	n/a
	Group 2	No. 1/No. 2	6	8	10	10	n/a	n/a	n/a
45.1 (3090)	Group 1	Sel Str	6	6	6	8	8	10	10
to	Group 1	No. 1/No. 2	6	6	8	10	10	n/a	n/a
50 (3425)	Group 2	Sel Str	6	6	8	10	10	n/a	n/a
	Group 2	No. 1/No. 2	6	8	10	10	n/a	n/a	n/a

Notes:
1. 4 is a 38 x 89mm stud (2 x 4 in.)
2. 6 is a 38 x 140mm stud (2 x 6 in.)
3. 8 is a 38 x 184mm stud (2 x 8 in.)
4. 10 is a 38 x 235mm stud (2 x 10 in.)
5. Species Group 1 is S-P-F, D.Fir-L, Hem-Fir
6. Species Group 2 is Northern Species Group
7. For the above calculations a suspended joist depth of 200mm (8 in.) and a cantilever length of 500mm (20 in.) was assumed.

PWF Stud Selection Tables

3.6m 200mm

Suspended Wood Floor

Stud length = 3.6m (12 ft.)
Stud spacing = 200mm (8 in.)

Vertical load range kN/m (plf)	Species	Grade	Backfill height, m (ft.-in.) 1.8 (6-0)	2.1 (7-0)	2.4 (8-0)	2.7 (9-0)	3 (10-0)	3.2 (10-6)	3.3 (11-0)	3.5 (11-6)
15 (1030)	Group 1	Sel Str	4	4	6	6	8	8	8	8
to	Group 1	No. 1/No. 2	4	6	6	6	8	8	10	10
20 (1370)	Group 2	Sel Str	4	6	6	8	8	8	8	10
	Group 2	No. 1/No. 2	6	6	6	8	10	10	10	n/a
20.1 (1375)	Group 1	Sel Str	4	4	6	6	8	8	8	8
to	Group 1	No. 1/No. 2	4	6	6	6	8	8	10	10
25 (1715)	Group 2	Sel Str	4	6	6	8	8	8	10	10
	Group 2	No. 1/No. 2	6	6	6	8	10	10	10	n/a
25.1 (1720)	Group 1	Sel Str	4	4	6	6	8	8	8	8
to	Group 1	No. 1/No. 2	4	6	6	6	8	8	10	10
30 (2055)	Group 2	Sel Str	6	6	6	8	8	8	10	10
	Group 2	No. 1/No. 2	6	6	6	8	10	10	10	n/a
30.1 (2060)	Group 1	Sel Str	4	6	6	6	8	8	8	8
to	Group 1	No. 1/No. 2	6	6	6	8	8	8	10	10
35 (2400)	Group 2	Sel Str	6	6	6	8	8	8	10	10
	Group 2	No. 1/No. 2	6	6	6	8	10	10	10	n/a
35.1 (2405)	Group 1	Sel Str	4	6	6	6	8	8	8	8
to	Group 1	No. 1/No. 2	6	6	6	8	8	8	10	10
40 (2740)	Group 2	Sel Str	6	6	6	8	8	8	10	10
	Group 2	No. 1/No. 2	6	6	8	8	10	10	10	n/a
40.1 (2750)	Group 1	Sel Str	6	6	6	6	8	8	8	8
to	Group 1	No. 1/No. 2	6	6	6	8	8	10	10	10
45 (3085)	Group 2	Sel Str	6	6	6	8	8	8	10	10
	Group 2	No. 1/No. 2	6	6	8	8	10	10	10	n/a
45.1 (3090)	Group 1	Sel Str	6	6	6	6	8	8	8	8
to	Group 1	No. 1/No. 2	6	6	6	8	8	10	10	10
50 (3425)	Group 2	Sel Str	6	6	6	8	8	10	10	10
	Group 2	No. 1/No. 2	6	6	8	8	10	10	n/a	n/a

Notes:
1. 4 is a 38 x 89mm stud (2 x 4 in.)
2. 6 is a 38 x 140mm stud (2 x 6 in.)
3. 8 is a 38 x 184mm stud (2 x 8 in.)
4. 10 is a 38 x 235mm stud (2 x 10 in.)
5. Species Group 1 is S-P-F, D.Fir-L, Hem-Fir
6. Species Group 2 is Northern Species Group
7. For the above calculations a suspended joist depth of 200mm (8 in.) and a cantilever length of 500mm (20 in.) was assumed.

A.2 Design Assumptions

Tabular data and figures in this publication are based on the general principles in CAN3/CSA-O86.1 with the following assumptions. For conditions that surpass these assumptions, the PWF should be designed by a structural engineer according to standards CAN/CSA-O86.1 and CSA S406. The engineer should also inspect the PWF to ensure that it has been installed properly.

Item	Assumption	
Soil bearing capacity	75 kN/m^2 (1500 lb/ft^2)	
Clear spans for floors	max. 5m (16'-5") or less, to centre support max. 8m (26'-3") or less, no centre support	
Floor live load	1.9 kN/m^2 (40 lb/ft^2) for first floor and suspended floor 1.4 kN/m^2 (30 lb/ft^2) for second storey floor	
Foundation Wall Heights	2.4 to 3.0m (8 to 10 ft) (3.0 to 3.6m (10 to 12 ft) for suspended floor)	
Top of granular drainage layer to top of suspended wood floor	600mm (24in.)	
Lateral load from soil pressure	equivalent to fluid pressure of 4.7 kN/m^2 per metre of depth (30 lb/ft^2 per foot of depth)	
Specified roof load	1.0 kN/m^2 (21 lb/ft^2) 1.5 kN/m^2 (31 lb/ft^2) 2.0 kN/m^2 (42 lb/ft^2), 2.5 kN/m^2 (52 lb/ft^2) 3.0 kN/m^2 (63 lb/ft^2)	
Roof loads	Roof loads are clear span with 600mm (24in.) overhang and all roof loads are carried to the exterior walls	
Dead loads	Roof	0.50 kN/m^2 (10.5 lb/ft^2)
	Floor	0.47 kN/m^2 (10 lb/ft^2)
	Wall (with siding)	0.32 kN/m^2 (6.5 lb/ft^2)
	Wall (with masonry veneer)	1.94 kN/m^2 (40.5 lb/ft^2)
	Foundation wall	0.27 kN/m^2 (5.5 lb/ft^2)
	Partitions	0.20 kN/m^2 (4 lb/ft^2)
Modification factors	Duration of load, K_D 0.65 for lateral soil loads 1.00 for live and snow loads (combined with dead loads)	
	System factor, K_h 1.40 for bending and shear 1.10 for compression parallel to grain	
	Service condition, K_s 1.00 for studs and fasteners 0.80 for plywood strength 0.85 for plywood stiffness	
	Preservative treatment factor, K_t = 1.00	
	Probability factor to reflect likelihood of full design live loads on roof and floors at the same time, = 0.80	
	Plywood end use factor, K_f 1.15 for panel bending and planar shear 1.00 for other properties	
Maximum deflections	L/300 for studs	
	L/180 for plywood	
Soil backfill height	Soil backfill height around the perimeter of the foundation is uniform, varying by no more than 600mm (24 in.), or provisions for unequal backfill heights given in Chapter 6 are to be followed.	

A.3 Unequal Backfill Tables (Imperial measure)

Table 6.3c
Perimeter nail spacings for differential backfill heights

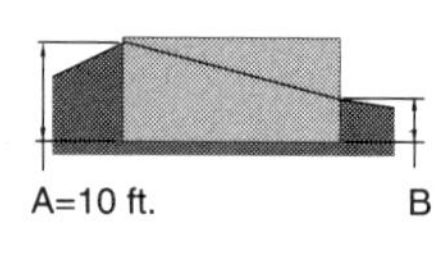

Backfill A = 10 ft.	Perimeter nail spacings, (in.)					
	L/W = 0.4		L/W = 0.6		L/W = 0.8	
	Nail length		Nail length		Nail length	
Backfill B (ft.)	2.5 in.	3 in.	2.5 in.	3 in.	2.5 in.	3 in.
0 to 3	4	4	2.5	2.5	2	2.5
3.1 to 5	4	6	2.5	4	2	2.5
5.1 to 6	4	6	2.5	4	2.5	2.5
6.1 to 7	6	6	4	4	2.5	2.5
7.1 to 8	6	6	4	4	2.5	4
8.1 or higher	6	6	6	6	6	6

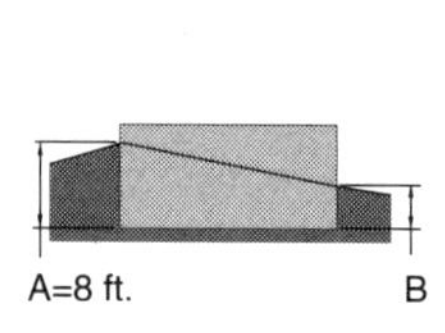

Backfill A = 8 ft.	Perimeter nail spacings, (in.)					
	L/W = 0.6		L/W = 1.0		L/W = 1.4	
	Nail length		Nail length		Nail length	
Backfill B (ft.)	2.5 in.	3 in.	2.5 in.	3 in.	2.5 in.	3 in.
0 to 2	4	4	2.5	4	2.5	2.5
2.1 to 4	4	6	2.5	4	2.5	2.5
4.1 to 5	4	6	4	4	2.5	2.5
5.1 to 6	6	6	4	6	2.5	4
6.1 or higher	6	6	6	6	6	6

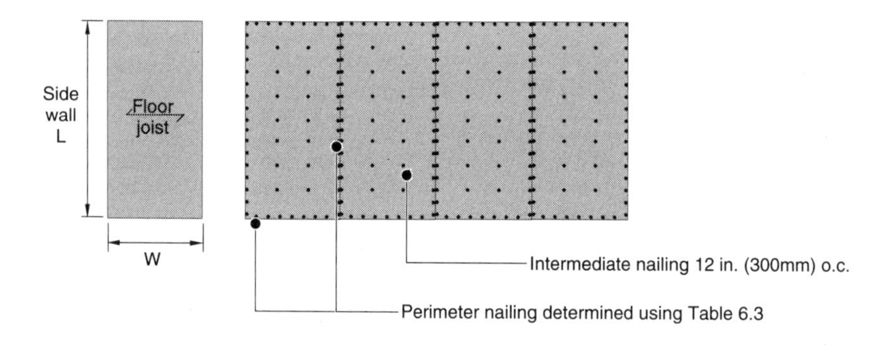

Table 6.3d
Perimeter nail spacings for differential backfill heights

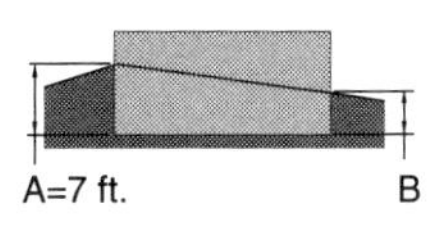

Backfill A = 7 ft.	Perimeter nail spacings, (in.)					
	L/W = 1.0		L/W = 1.4		L/W = 1.8	
	Nail length		Nail length		Nail length	
Backfill B (ft.)	2.5 in.	3 in.	2.5 in.	3 in.	2.5 in.	3 in.
0 to 2	4	6	2.5	4	2.5	2.5
2.1 to 3	4	6	4	4	2.5	2.5
3.1 to 4	4	6	4	4	2.5	4
4.1 to 5	6	6	4	6	2.5	4
5.1 or higher	6	6	6	6	6	6

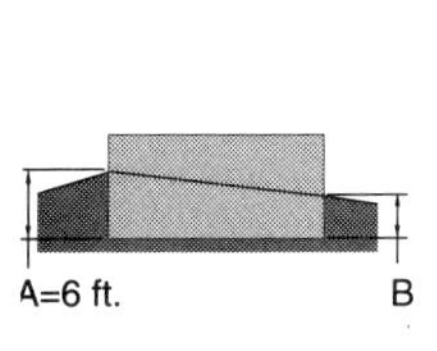

Backfill A = 6 ft.	Perimeter nail spacings, (in.)					
	L/W = 1.6		L/W = 2.0		L/W = 2.5	
	Nail length		Nail length		Nail length	
Backfill B (ft.)	2.5 in.	3 in.	2.5 in.	3 in.	2.5 in.	3 in.
0 to 3	4	6	4	4	2.5	4
3.1 to 4	6	6	4	6	4	4
4.1 or higher	6	6	6	6	6	6

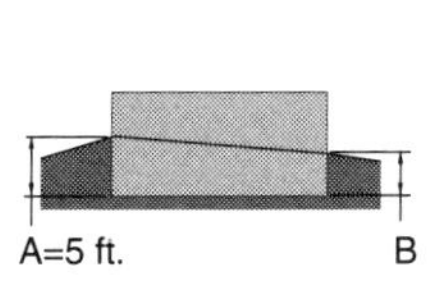

Backfill A = 5 ft.	Perimeter nail spacings, (in.)					
	L/W = 2.0		L/W = 2.5		L/W = 3.0	
	Nail length		Nail length		Nail length	
Backfill B (ft.)	2.5 in.	3 in.	2.5 in.	3 in.	2.5 in.	3 in.
0 to 3	6	6	6	6	4	6
3.1 or higher	6	6	6	6	6	6

Notes:
1. This table appears in chapter 6 in metric units.
2. All panel edges backed with pressure treated 2 x 4 in. (38 x 89mm) framing or wider. Sheathing installed either horizontally or vertically. Space nails at 12 in. (300mm) on centre along intermediate studs.
3. For L/W ratios less than the lowest ratios listed, the nail spacings shown for the lowest ratios may be used.

Notes

Notes

Notes